DORM

DORMICE

Pat Morris
with illustrations by **Guy Troughton**

Whittet Books

Dedication

This book is dedicated to the late Doug Woods, whose contribution to work on dormice was fundamental. His unfailing enthusiasm and dedication did so much to establish our early fieldwork, nest box monitoring and the captive breeding programme upon which the reintroduction projects have been based. We, and the dormice, owe him a great deal.

Contents

Illustrator's acknowledgments

Pat Morris has been tutor, mentor and friend to me over many years now. When he asked me to illustrate Hedgehogs in 1982 it was both the start of my career as a wildlife artist and the first of many *Whittet* books to come. I am greatly indebted to him and it has been an enormous pleasure to work with Pat again on this book.

I would also like to thank my mother Val who not only encouraged me in the precarious business of being an artist but actively collected dead specimens for me to draw, and my sister Trish who put up with the smell.

My love and thanks too to my wife Ellie and sons John and Max for their love and support and for tolerating my long hours working in the studio.

Introduction

Dormice are different from other mice. In fact they are rather special creatures, as this book will show. In Britain we have only two species, but they are as different from each other as chalk and cheese. So this book mostly treats them separately.

The native British dormouse often occurs among hazels, hence the common name 'hazel dormouse'. It used to be found frequently during hedging and coppicing work and children often kept them as pets in Victorian times. However, it has been getting progressively rarer over the past hundred years, with nobody really noticing because it is a very elusive creature. It is small, almost wholly nocturnal and lives most of its life up in the trees. Small wonder that it is rarely seen. It also does not normally enter the sort of traps that are used for studying small mammals, nor is it often caught by cats or owls. Consequently hardly anything was known about its ecology until quite recently. Even the average body weight of a British dormouse was unknown – the *Handbook of British Mammals*, published in the mid 1970s, gave figures from German dormice kept in captivity more than a hundred years ago (and evidently somewhat overfed!)

The sheer elusiveness of this creature has meant that very few studies have ever been made of its ecology, here or in the other countries where it occurs. Elaine Hurrell published two small books (in 1962 and 1980) based on observations of captive animals and some studies in the Devon countryside around her home. Apart from these and minor notes in local natural history publications, only two scientific studies were published about British hazel dormice in the whole of the twentieth century, before our own work began.

About 1983 I decided it was time to try and find ways to study the dormouse and began by devising a trap that would catch them alive and unharmed. I thought that maybe dormice didn't like smooth metal traps, maybe they were claustrophobic and didn't want to enter small tunnels on the ground, perhaps they didn't like corn as bait either. Scientists aren't supposed to think like this, pretending to be animals, but who cares if it helps solve the problem? I built some simple wire traps with small plastic pots inside to protect the animals from wind and rain, baited them with apple, set them in trees and soon started to capture dormice, the first time that anyone had succeeded in doing that on a regular basis. Dormice were thus added to the hedgehogs, red squirrels and water voles in our research programme at Royal Holloway College.

By a fortunate coincidence, Doug Woods, an energetic member of the Somerset Wildlife Trust, had also been thinking about dormice. He devised some special nest boxes intended to be attractive to this species and put them up in woods near Cheddar. One day he took me there and we saw four dormice without walking more than fifty metres from my car! Doug agreed to join forces and we were in business, with the tools to study these elusive creatures at last. Later I was asked by the Government's conservation agency to begin a three-year programme of research to find out why dormice had become rare and devise methods to save them from dying out altogether. They provided the cash, supplemented by the World Wide Fund for Nature (and later the Vincent Wildlife Trust) and the 'Dormouse Project' began in 1984. Ten years later, the project was to become one of the highlights of British natural history, with dozens of local dormouse conservation projects established all over the country.

It was a tall order to find out, within three years, everything significant about a species whose biology was so poorly known. I needed someone who would dedicate himself totally to doing the necessary fieldwork to find out what makes dormice tick. This would require long and lonely hours of radio tracking into the small hours of the morning. It would need stamina, ingenuity in fixing dodgy equipment, and a thorough understanding of woodland ecology. It would be a seven days a week job, in all weathers and with little help. Paul Bright rose to this challenge magnificently and most of what we now know about the intricate ecology of the dormouse is as a result of his painstaking fieldwork. We marooned Paul in a caravan at a pig farm in the Mendips for three years. There was nothing much else to do except get on with the research, and the results came in thick and fast. The data Paul collected also required a thorough understanding of statistics, without which we could not be sure that our studies were actually meaningful and not simply the result of chance events. Early on Paul asked me to buy him an expensive statistics book, which I did rather grudgingly. It was one of the best investments of £30 I ever made.

Once it became widely known that there were people at Royal Holloway College studying dormice, we began to get letters and phone calls about the other species, the edible dormouse. Unlike the hazel dormouse, this one is not a cute creature at all. It is big, noisy, bad tempered and bites like hell. Worse, it damages foresters' trees and also enters people's houses and creates havoc there. In parts of the Chilterns where it is common, people have been driven to distraction by its activities and they wanted help. Nobody else was studying this beast, so the enquiries came to me in the belief that one dormouse must be much like another. Thus I became drawn into working on the edible dormouse as well.

So, this book is an account of the fascinating intricacies of these two species, similar yet so different. Our work on the small native dormouse has resulted in much public interest and many valuable spin-offs in terms of wildlife conservation. It provides a beacon for others in Europe to follow, where the species is widespread, but still poorly known. Conversely, the edible dormouse has been better studied in other countries and we have begun to absorb useful lessons from abroad which may one day help to provide a solution to some of the problems this animal causes in Britain. The exchange of ideas has been helped a lot by a series of international dormouse 'workshops'. Far from going to sleep, everyone is able to exchange ideas and information and there is now an extensive network of researchers right across the Continent, all dormousing away, at last unravelling the secrets of these curious creatures. Now we have a National Dormouse Monitoring Programme (still the only system for monitoring numbers of any British mammal nationwide), a reintroduction programme to restore hazel dormice to counties where they had become extinct and now lots of basic information about the biology of dormice such that we now know more about these animals than we do about many species that are actually more common. A few years ago nobody would have believed it possible.

In fact it wouldn't have been possible but for the help we have received from scores of people. Countless volunteers go out regularly to check nest boxes and send us their data, as some of them have for more than ten years. My students have provided a valuable pool of talent from which I have drawn many temporary assistants to help with radio tracking and other fieldwork, among them Paul Bright himself and the indefatigable Don MacPherson. Paige Mitchell must have inspected more square metres of woodland on her knees than anyone else alive, carrying out gnawed-nut surveys, and Andrew Hoodless managed our first radio tracking studies of edible dormice, whilst setting up a highly acclaimed TV programme on those animals. Each of the reintroduction projects has also required lots of help, starting with Doug Woods and others in the Dormouse Captive Breeders Group and including many different teams of volunteers to manage the release cages and ensure the continued feeding of dormice for weeks at a stretch. My wife Mary has also been a constant source of support. It would be impossible here to name all those who have helped us, but this book and a whole string of scientific papers are testimony to the huge support we have received from so many people. I am very grateful for that and pleased that between us we have now made the hazel dormouse one of the best-known of Britain's small mammals. My retirement has cut short what might have been possible with the other species but, again, thanks to stalwart volunteer assistants like Brian and Sian Barton, fieldwork will continue and we have already amassed more information about edible dormice in Britain than anyone would have thought possible, especially given the shortage of research money to work on this species! Fortunately, the dormouse momentum is being maintained through the support of the Mammals Trust (UK) and the People's Trust for Endangered Species, enabling research and practical conservation to continue and helping still more people to see and learn about these fascinating animals.

Pat Morris
2011

What's special about dormice?

Dormice form a whole family of rodents all their own. Ordinary mice (and rats) comprise the family Muridae containing many hundreds of species. Squirrels are Sciuridae and dormice are different again, classified in a family called the Gliridae. There are about twenty living species, half of them from Africa. The others are widely scattered from Spain to Japan. They all have big black eyes and soft fine fur. Characteristically, dormice have fluffy, squirrel-like tails, the only small mammals thus endowed. Unlike the tail in other rodents, that of the dormouse is rather delicate. The skin is thin and if gripped by a predator (or human or another dormouse) the skin comes off, leaving the tail bones exposed. These soon dry out and drop off, so it is not uncommon to see a dormouse with a truncated tail. This is true of both hazel and edible dormice. Truncated tails are quite common in the latter.

Dormice also have four molar teeth (instead of the three that are normally found in rodents) with transverse ridges instead of knobbly lumps as in mice or zig zag ridges as in voles and hamsters. Their feet

Dormice are agile creatures, with strong gripping feet.

are extraordinary too. They have gripping pads that make the feet feel almost sticky and greatly assist when climbing and gripping smooth surfaces. Needle-sharp claws can get a hold on even quite smooth surfaces. The hind feet can be rotated at the ankle, allowing the animal to hang head downwards, suspended by its hind claws, an ability shared with squirrels. These features constitute adaptations to a highly arboreal way of life, in which the animals scamper about among tree branches with amazing agility. Dormice are extremely agile, climbing and jumping among leaves and branches at an astonishing speed, even though they are active in almost total darkness.

Another anatomical distinction is that dormice do not have a caecum, the part of the digestive system that normally processes leaves and grass in other mammals. This seems like a very obscure anatomical detail, but as we shall see later it is in fact probably the key single feature that governs the whole ecology of our dormice in Britain. It is one of the factors that has led indirectly to the decline of the 'common' dormouse in this country, because it means the animals have to be food specialists. They cannot survive just by eating grass or leaves.

Dormice are interesting mammals from a variety of viewpoints, relevant to many different fields of biology. They are an ancient group of mammals that formed one of the basic types of rodent long ago. They were once widespread and diverse in terms of numbers of species, far more so than they are today. Their fossil remains provide an insight into the early evolution and diversity of rodents and there has been much discussion about the evolution and relationships of the whole rodent group, based on studies of fossil teeth, particularly those of dormice. However, we now have access to the new tools offered by molecular biology, that provide fresh evidence of how various mammal groups are related to each other, confirming, adjusting or even contradicting existing ideas. This has resulted in much abstruse debate among specialist zoologists.

Dormice also have a specialised physiology and many of them adjust their body mechanisms profoundly in winter and go into deep hibernation. This raises questions about how and why hibernation evolved and how it is controlled. Hibernation is a winter phenomenon, shared with some other groups of mammals, but many dormice also

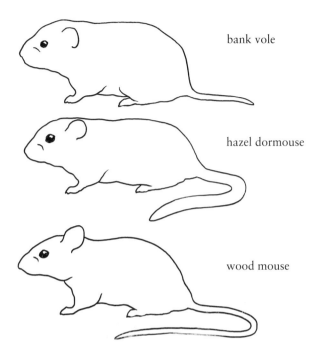

Size comparisons.

frequently undergo additional periods of torpor during the active season. Their body temperature falls substantially, evidently to reduce the energy cost of remaining warm blooded during periods of bad weather and food shortage. Few other mammals do this (apart from some bats), as it gets in the way of successful breeding. During both hibernation and torpor, dormice abandon the advantages of warm bloodedness, a key feature of mammals that contributes so much to their success. This raises important questions, for both physiologists and ecologists, about how and why these unusual physiological adjustments occur.

Dormice are naturally rare and far less abundant than typical mousy rodents, for example. This raises interesting ecological questions about why this should be so. In recent times, natural scarcity has often been made worse by environmental damage caused by human activities. As a result, several species are now regarded as rare or endangered, leading to conservation-related research and active habitat management to assist their survival. Their sensitivity to both climate and other environmental factors also means that dormice are important indicators of environmental change, again a topic worthy of considerable research. Scarcity has led to legal protection, and international agreement, in the form of the Berne Convention, protects dormice throughout Europe. Yet, paradoxically, one species (the edible dormouse) is often regarded as an agricultural and domestic pest, and it is also hunted for food in some countries.

So, dormice are interesting, distinctive and different.

Fossil dormice

Dormice are the most ancient group of rodents still living today. They date back more than 40 million years. Fossil dormice are not normally found whole, but their teeth are found in deposits of earth trapped in cracks among rocks, perhaps where the animals died long ago or where their remains were left by predators. An exception is a single animal pickled in a bed of oily tar-like material from Germany. It is the oldest known dormouse called Eogliravus wildi. *Its body is complete enough to tell that it was a tree-dwelling animal with a fluffy tail that fed on fruits and seeds, remains of which are still present in the stomach after 50 million years. Fossil dormouse teeth are occasionally found in Britain.*

Who's who

The dormouse family (Gliridae) consists of only twenty species, about half of which are found in Africa and the rest occur from western Europe to Japan. The species form seven groups called genera. Most of the genera have only a single species.

One species of dormouse (*Glirulus japonicus*) occurs in Japan, where it lives in forests on steep mountainsides. It resembles the British dormouse, but is greyer, with longer hairs and a black stripe down its back. It seems to live a similar sort of life too. Since this species occurs only in Japan and nowhere else, and it has lived there for millions of years, the Japanese Government declared it a 'National Monument'. This significantly raises its profile and improves the chances of successful habitat conservation to preserve the Japanese dormouse, and lots of other things that live with it. A former schoolteacher, Shusaku Minato, now acts as 'Mr Dormouse', promoting dormice on television and organizing important educational and conservation projects based at a dormouse museum facing Mount Fuji. This is an excellent example of just how much can be achieved by focusing on a single species.

Several species of the genus *Graphiurus* inhabit large areas of Africa. These African dormice are plain pale grey and look like small squirrels. They are found in forests and also in thorny scrub.

Otherwise, the dormice are essentially a Palaearctic group, being

Japanese dormouse –
Glirulus

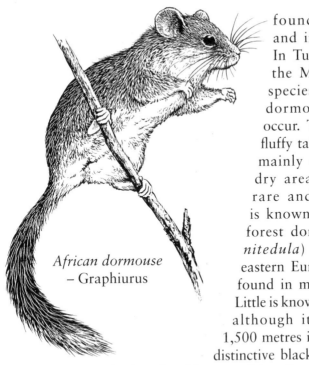

African dormouse
– Graphiurus

found across Europe and into western Asia. In Turkey and parts of the Middle East, some species of mouse-tailed dormouse (*Myomimus*) occur. These do not have fluffy tails and seem to live mainly on the ground in dry areas. They are very rare and almost nothing is known about them. The forest dormouse (*Dryomys nitedula*) occurs in south-eastern Europe and is mainly found in mature forest areas. Little is known about its ecology, although it does live up to 1,500 metres in the Alps. It has a distinctive black mask through the eyes, making it look rather like a traditionally dressed bandit. The garden dormouse (*Eliomys quercinus*) also has a prominent black mask and its tail is less bushy than that of other dormice. Instead it is a striking black above and white below. Garden dormice spend a lot of their time on the ground but can still climb incredibly well. I have watched one scale a gloss-painted door post, brick walls are no obstacle at all.

Garden dormice pose interesting questions related to their distribution. They appear to have colonised north Africa by spreading round both ends of the Mediterranean, to form

Mouse-tailed dormouse –
Myomimus

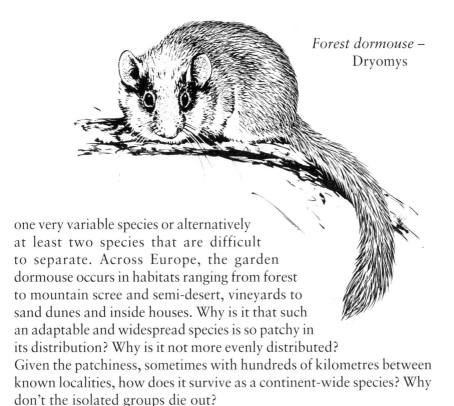

Forest dormouse –
Dryomys

one very variable species or alternatively
at least two species that are difficult
to separate. Across Europe, the garden
dormouse occurs in habitats ranging from forest
to mountain scree and semi-desert, vineyards to
sand dunes and inside houses. Why is it that such
an adaptable and widespread species is so patchy in
its distribution? Why is it not more evenly distributed?
Given the patchiness, sometimes with hundreds of kilometres between
known localities, how does it survive as a continent-wide species? Why
don't the isolated groups die out?

Muscardinus avellanarius, the hazel dormouse, is widespread in
Europe, but it is the only species within that genus and in many areas
it is the only type of dormouse present. It is strongly associated with
woodland edges, shrubs and scrub. These are usually temporary
habitats where continuous habitat corridors are essential to link
scattered local populations and enable their survival. *Muscardinus* is
particularly associated with hazel and its numbers appear generally
stable from year to year, perhaps being mainly affected by weather and
habitat quality. The edible dormouse (*Glis glis*) is also a unique species
within its own genus. It seems to favour mature forests, particularly
where there are plenty of beech trees. Its reproduction is strongly linked
to the production of beech nuts, which varies a lot from year to year,
leading to huge fluctuations in population density of edible dormice
and periodic failure to reproduce at all.

In Britain we have two species of dormouse. The native one

Garden dormouse –
Eliomys

(*Muscardinus avellanarius*) is often called the hazel dormouse, because of its strong association with hazel woods. Its scientific name reflects this: avellana is the Latin name for the hazel. This animal is about the size of a large mouse, normally weighing 15-30 g. Adults are about 8 cm long, with fluffy tails of similar length. Sometimes the tail is tipped with white. The fur is a fine golden brown or yellow colour, often with a white belly. The ears and eyes are very prominent and there are big whiskers on the muzzle. The hazel dormouse is called 'native' because it was one of the animals that reached Britain by natural spread as the climate improved at the end of the last Ice Age, and before rising sea levels prevented any more mammals from moving into this country from the Continent. It is now widespread in southern counties, although nowhere common. It is found from Cornwall to Kent, north to Shropshire and Northamptonshire. Beyond that, there are probably only about three or four sites in the whole of northern England.

The other species in Britain is the edible dormouse (*Glis glis*), also called the fat dormouse. This is nearly ten times bigger than the hazel dormouse, being more like a small squirrel. It is a uniform grey, with a creamy white underside and plain chocolate brown tail. There are dark areas around the eyes which create a slightly sinister appearance. As with other dormice, the fur is soft and the feet have extraordinary gripping powers. This dormouse is an introduced species, brought here in 1902. It has spread through the woodlands of the Chilterns in Hertfordshire and Buckinghamshire, with a few scattered localities elsewhere. However, it is essentially restricted in its distribution to an area of perhaps 50 square kilometres, about 100 kilometres north-west of London. Deliberate releases have enabled it to reach other places (the New Forest for example) and its future distribution may become much extended as it is illegally released in other parts of the country.

There are no dormice in Ireland or Scotland: an attempted introduction to Ireland failed long ago.

SUMMARY OF THE DIFFERENCES BETWEEN THE TWO BRITISH SPECIES OF DORMICE

Hazel dormouse, *Muscardinus avellanarius*	Edible dormouse, *Glis glis*
Native, been here since the last Ice Age	Introduced, 1902
Rare, but widespread in southern counties	Only in the Chilterns area of Buckingham-shire, Berkshire, and Hertfordshire (where it is often common)
Overall golden yellow, except for white belly.	Grey/dark brown, white belly. Often with black around the eyes and at the base of the whiskers
Mouse size (10-30 g). Head & body length about 50 mm, tail 50 mm	Almost squirrel size (50-250 g). Head & body length about 150-175 mm, tail 120-150 mm
Lives mainly in under storey, hedges	Inhabits mature high forest and shrubs (especially hazel) (especially beech) and plantations

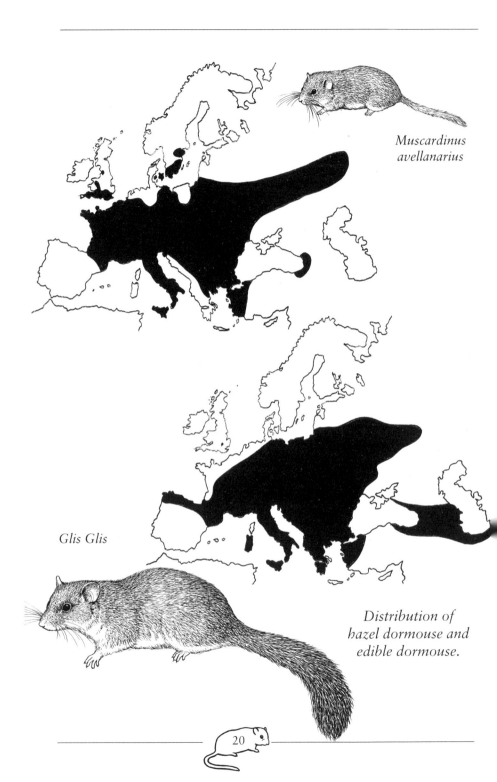

Muscardinus avellanarius

Glis Glis

Distribution of hazel dormouse and edible dormouse.

The dormouse year

Both our British dormice hibernate. They begin in the autumn, but exactly when depends on the weather and the supplies of food. In mild weather, and especially if fruits and nuts remain available, both species can be found active as late as November or even occasionally in December. In years when there has been little food or breeding activity edible dormice may begin hibernating as early as late August. Generally, it is the older, fatter animals that hibernate first, with young and small animals going down later. Hazel dormice vary according to latitude, with those living in the south of England probably having an extended activity season compared to those living further north. The trigger for hibernation is low temperatures combined with a sharp decline in food availability when the first frosts come.

Arousal probably takes place in stages, with the animals going back into hibernation again in bad weather, following brief periods of activity in the spring. About April (or later further north) hazel dormice cease to hibernate and are probably active every night. Edible dormice seem to be active in buildings as early as March sometimes, but rarely show up out in the woods until well into May or even June.

Both species are then active throughout the summer, although sleeping during the day of course. In addition, the hazel dormouse also enters a torpid state (especially in early summer, see page 55), but the edible dormouse rarely does this.

Both species tend to breed later than other woodland rodents. Hazel dormice sometimes have young as early as June in the south of England, but usually not until July. Edible dormice living indoors may breed early, but out in the woods they rarely produce young earlier than August. In both species, the young have to grow fast and fatten up for winter at the same time. The adults of both species accumulate fat very rapidly in the autumn, sometimes almost doubling their weight in a matter of only a month or so, before going into hibernation.

The annual cycle for both species is likely to be very different in southern Europe, where the climate is different. In particular, the summers are very hot and dry and some animals may aestivate (a form of 'summer hibernation') where they give up activity and go torpid until more congenial conditions return in the autumn. Winters are likely to be brief, leading to shorter periods spent in true hibernation. In some areas of central Italy the dormice seem not to hibernate at all. However, there has been relatively little research done into the differences within European populations, especially comparing north with south. It is likely that there are north-south differences in litter size and also differences in the proportion of females that successfully rear second litters in the same season.

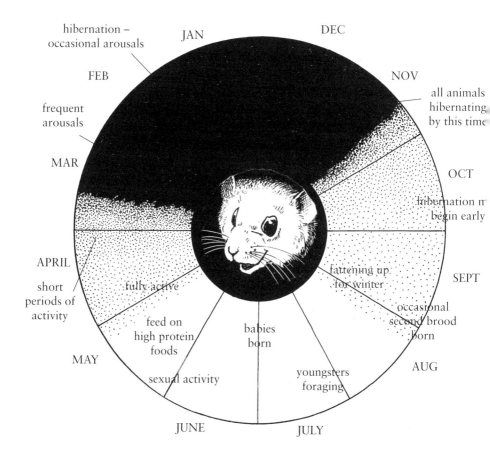

The dormouse year.

THE HAZEL DORMOUSE
The disappearing dormouse

Everyone knows what the hazel dormouse looks like, with its chubby face, golden yellow fur and big black eyes. Nevertheless, few people have actually seen one. This applies even to the professional zoologists who may spend their lives studying woodland mammals without ever catching sight of a dormouse.

Muscardinus is a small, nocturnal and arboreal mammal. It is therefore unlikely to be seen very often, even where it is relatively abundant. It is therefore possible that this elusiveness has created a false impression of rarity. Maybe they are actually quite common animals, but people just don't notice them? We can be pretty certain that this is not the case because there is now plenty of evidence that this species really is scarce and is becoming more so as its geographical range contracts southwards. In Victorian times, dormice used to be commonly found in the course of woodland management operations, a situation that contrasts with the present where few people have ever seen one. In the 1880s a keen naturalist by the name of Rope wrote to all the notable observers he could think of in different parts of the country, asking whether dormice were found locally. From their replies he was able to construct a very valuable description of the distribution of dormice in the late 19th century, which we can compare with the results of more recent surveys. Basically it appears that dormice did occur in almost every English and Welsh county, almost as far north as the Scottish border.

Since Rope's time, people have often suggested that dormice have become rare, but there has been little by way of actual proof nor much evidence as to the cause. What is very clear, however, is that the dormouse has become extremely rare or even extinct in many places where it was formerly present. This is particularly noticeable in the north of England. Old natural history books often provide detailed comments about the status of dormice at the beginning of the twentieth century, but even then they seemed to be scarce in northern counties. By the 1920s, local naturalists in many areas were telling similar stories to the effect that dormice used to be quite plentiful, but had become less so and had now vanished. A typical account published in 1934 said, 'Whilst thirty or more years ago one used to see dormice in our district (Hitchin, Hertfordshire) rather frequently, now they are few and far between'. This comment was supported by observations from various local people. In the 19th century dormice were certainly present at least as far north as the River Tyne, but in eastern England there are no confirmed sightings from north of the Humber since 1960 (although one small population still exists near Hexham in Northumberland, the most northerly occurrence of this species in Britain, with a few more in Cumbria). During the late 1970s, Elaine Hurrell carried out a distribution survey for the Mammal Society and confirmed that dormice still existed in these two northern counties, but she failed to find any recent evidence of dormice in seven counties where Rope had reported them a century earlier (Cheshire, Derbyshire, Lincolnshire, Norfolk, Staffordshire, Warwickshire and Yorkshire). It was presumed that dormice had become extinct in these areas.

The dormouse appears to be absent from Norfolk although it was reported to be there in the 1840s. Later, the eminent Norfolk writer and naturalist A. H. Patterson wrote that it was 'not known to me personally'. Extensive efforts in modern times have failed to confirm any recent record of dormice in Norfolk. By comparison, reports of dormice in Suffolk and Essex have been quite numerous, but the species

A disappearing dormouse.

still seems to have declined there recently, suggesting that it is slowly dying out in East Anglia.

The tiny cluster of dormouse records from Cumbria are focussed on only three small areas, particularly in the sheltered Duddon

Legal protection

The hazel dormouse was listed on Schedule 6 of the Wildlife & Countryside Act in 1981, giving it partial protection. It was granted full protection as a Schedule 5 species in 1986. This was a pretty trivial change because protection was only provided against threats which are probably insignificant. Legal protection prevents trapping, killing and trade, but offers no defence against habitat loss. However, legal protection did at least draw attention to the uncertain future for the dormouse and encouraged research and conservation activities. But legal protection alone offers no way of consolidating its distribution or preventing further slide towards extinction. Nevertheless, it is good that the dormouse is listed alongside the otter, red squirrel, pine marten and bats as a fully protected species, clearly and properly identifying it as one of Britain's most precious animals. The hazel dormouse has now been elevated to the status of a European Protected Species. This means that you must not catch dormice or disturb them in nest boxes or interfere with their habitat. In theory, that makes forestry, hedgerow management and even coppicing for dormouse conservation potentially illegal. In practice these activities remain acceptable provided that appropriate care is taken not to cause significant damage at the population level. Nevertheless, it's now almost illegal to say 'boo' to a dormouse, and there are significant fines for anyone convicted of deliberately or even carelessly interfering with them.

Wildlife protection regulations now require developers to carry out surveys and deal sympathetically with any dormice found in areas whose habitat is due to be altered or destroyed. 'Mitigation measures', compensating for damage to dormouse interests, have resulted in planting new hedges and thousands of young trees.

Where dormouse habitat needs to be cleared (e.g. for road widening) elaborate and expensive precautions have to be taken to avoid killing animals. Woodland clearance must be done in a special way to minimise damage to dormouse populations. Hedges must be planted to link up any isolated patches of habitat. After a century of losing out, the dormice now have the law on their side!

Valley. Certain areas like this enjoy favourable local conditions, while generally the Lake District climate is similar to elsewhere in northern England. The apparent absence of dormice between Cumbria and Shropshire is probably genuine. The animal seems to have died out in Cheshire, where it was already regarded as rare by 1910, although it had been common there in some areas in the nineteenth century (e.g. near Alderley in the 1870s). Today, there appears to be little suitable habitat remaining in that county.

Further evidence of decline comes from a big library search in which one of my students read all the local mammal reports published by naturalists during the twentieth century. Jane scanned over 3,000 volumes and noted how often the dormouse was reported in each decade since 1900. Few records of dormice emerged from northern counties and many reports explicitly indicated scarcity. These generally pessimistic comments contrasted with a comparative abundance of records and enthusiastic remarks in reports from Kent, Sussex, Wiltshire, Somerset and Devon. There was also clear evidence of declining status. In the 1930s, all the mammal reports examined mentioned dormice, but by the 1950s only 63% did so and by the 1970s the proportion was down to 46%.

Nevertheless, despite evidence of considerable decline, the hazel dormouse remains widespread and relatively numerous in some counties. For example, a detailed survey of 238 woodlands in Herefordshire found dormice to be widely distributed there and predicted that they still occur in 34% of the woodland areas of that county. Several surveys in Kent have found evidence of dormice in almost every wood and copse where searches have been made.

Overall, it seems clear that the dormouse has disappeared from about half its previous range, mostly in the north. Where it does still occur, its distribution is distinctly patchy and it is nowhere common. There is no evidence that it ever occurred in Scotland, and Welsh localities are few and far between. Some of the gaps in national distribution have now been filled by releasing a few captive bred animals, but it remains to be seen how widely they will manage to spread.

Signs of dormice and the Great Nut Hunt of 1993

Searching for dormice is a dead loss, so it is very difficult to carry out distribution surveys or to find out whether or not hazel dormice live in a particular place. Fortunately, years ago H.G. Hurrell had noticed that his captive dormice opened hazel nuts in a distinctive manner. Voles and wood mice eat hazels too, and all three gnaw a neat hole in the shell. However, mice and voles leave clear tooth marks that make a rough edge to the hole. The dormouse turns the nut sideways after gnawing into the shell and then uses its teeth in a scooping action to enlarge the hole. As a result, the hole becomes very smooth and almost perfectly circular. Any tooth marks present always run along inside the cut edge of the hole. With a magnifying glass these tooth marks can be used to distinguish 'dormouse nuts' from others. Squirrels eat a lot of hazel nuts too, but open the shells by cracking them apart. This leaves irregular shaped pieces, often with sharp jagged edges, quite unlike the neat smooth hole made by the dormouse.

The best time to look for the nuts is after about mid August, when the nuts are fresh. They can still be found well into the following year, but as time goes by they tend to rot and this gradually causes the tooth marks to become indistinct. It is difficult to recognise dormouse nuts that have been lying in the leaf litter for more than about eight months.

With practice, these diagnostic nuts can be used as a method for establishing the presence of dormice without actually seeing the animals. It is less easy to prove absence, but our studies show that searching three 5 x 5 metre squares under different hazel bushes, for 20 minutes each will almost certainly turn up evidence of dormice if they are present. If five such samples fail to find the distinctive nuts, then it is almost certain that dormice are not there.

In 1993 it was decided to organise a major public participation exercise, which we called 'The Great Nut Hunt'. The idea was to issue as many people as possible with an instruction kit telling them how to identify hazels, how to search for gnawed nuts and how to recognise those that had been opened by dormice. Any dormouse nuts they found were to be sent for checking by The Chief Nutter (me!). A special data sheet was also to be filled in showing what people did: where they looked, how long they searched and how many nuts they found. The report form also asked for a site name and map reference, so that a distribution map could be plotted later. Eleven thousand survey packs were distributed to schools, naturalists and the general public, including special badges saying 'I'm a Nutter'. (During a radio interview, I stuck one of these on the reporter. She forgot it was there and shortly afterwards rushed off to a hospital appointment, still labelled as a Nutter. I have not seen her since.) It was originally intended that The Great Nut Hunt would last six months, but nuts were still being sent in over a year later!

The Great Nut Hunt was a lot of fun. Over 6,000 people joined in and a good time was had by all. We were sent many lovingly wrapped samples of nut shells, packed in margarine pots, crisp packets, film containers and aspirin bottles. In many cases whole families and classes of school kids had searched their local woods, sometimes sending us packets of feathers and other interesting things when they had failed to find any dormouse nuts.

As a result of this exercise, more than a quarter of a million hazel nuts were inspected, from all over England and Wales. People sent in 1,878 report forms and hundreds of packets of nuts. We had teams of students opening the packets so that every nut, believed to have been gnawed by a dormouse, could be checked by me – all 13,171 of them.

The searchers found 172,644 gnawed nuts. Most of these were discarded by observers in the field as the work of squirrels, wood mice or bank voles. Of the 13,171 nuts submitted for confirmation that they had been opened by dormice, 63% proved to have been opened by squirrels. The 1,352 confirmed 'dormouse nuts' came from 235 observers, who thereby identified 334 dormouse sites in England and Wales. From these, a new and up-to-date distribution map could be created.

Instructions had been supplied in the survey packs, showing how to work out a map reference. This, we thought, would later enable us to create a new distribution map for the dormouse, based on the nuts sent in. Unfortunately, no map reference was supplied in many cases, although sometimes we could locate the site on a map ourselves. Worse was the inclusion of confident map references that turned out to be in the North Sea! Apparently some people had managed to get the instructions wrong. If some could, so might others. We therefore had to go through the whole lot and check every single map reference to be sure that it was probably accurate.

Dormouse sites were confirmed in 29 counties of England and Wales, with 24% of the total nuts coming from Devon. The proportion of sites in each county where dormice were found gives a rough idea of relative abundance. For example, in Kent and Sussex over 20% of the sites checked had evidence of dormice; 59% in Dorset and 47% in Devon, but in Cumbria only 1.6% of the sites yielded dormouse nuts. However, the effort expended in searching was not uniform, so these comparisons are not very reliable.

By recording the number of people searching and the time they took to find nuts we were able to make a rough comparison of success in detecting dormice in different places. For example, in Dorset it took 66 person-minutes to locate an actual dormouse nut, and only 60 in Somerset. In other counties it took more than twice as much effort to find a dormouse nut. The percentage of opened nuts that were confirmed as having been gnawed by dormice offered another indication of relative abundance. In most counties, especially in the north, fewer than 0.5% of the nuts had been opened by dormice, but in Dorset it was 2.47% and on the Isle of Wight it was 4.45%. Altogether, the evidence clearly showed that dormice are more abundant in the south of England, by a very long way.

Despite extensive searches, the existence of hazel dormice was not confirmed in any of the seven counties (Cheshire, Derbyshire, Lincolnshire, Norfolk, Staffordshire, Warwickshire and Yorkshire) where the Mammal Society survey by Hurrell and McIntosh had failed to find them twenty years earlier, despite their known presence in the 1880s. This suggests that dormice had indeed become locally extinct. This is particularly notable for Yorkshire, where at least 20 dormouse sites were known in the late 19th century. During the Great Nut Hunt, searches were made at 83 sites in that county, but no evidence of dormice was found, despite many hours of search effort and inspection

dormouse

smooth round hole,
tooth marks around,
inside edge of hole

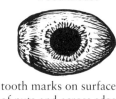
wood mouse

tooth marks on surface
of nuts and across edge
of hole

squirrel/woodpecker

nut shattered

bank vole
tooth marks across
edge of hole

wood mouse
hole often ragged,
not circular

tiny bored hole =
escaping weevil

Hazel nuts opened by different species.

of some 12,000 opened Yorkshire nuts.

The good news is that signs of hazel dormice were found in every county of Wales. This is particularly pleasing as there had been no records from the Dolgellau and Conway Valley areas of North Wales for more than half a century. The Great Nut Hunt put them back on the map!

Volunteers had contributed a total of more than 6,100 hours to this nationwide search. This is the equivalent of hiring someone to do the job, working a 40-hour week, for three years. So, this exercise, using volunteers, constituted a highly cost-effective way of surveying for this elusive and patchily distributed animal and we were very grateful to all who had taken part.

The quantity of information gained in the Great Nut Hunt should be viewed in the context that the national Biological Records Centre received only 52 dormouse records in the 15 years 1980-1994. Since the survey technique is simple it could be repeated in the future as part of national or local monitoring dormouse programmes. A 'surveillance survey', revisiting the positive sites from the Great Nut Hunt in 20 years' time, would indicate the rate at which dormouse populations were still being lost locally.

Additional Nut Hunts in 2001 and 2009 resulted in thousands more nuts being sent to the Chief Nutter for identification, and various local surveys have also been undertaken, focussing on woods in Wales and the north of England. We now have a much more accurate idea of where dormice occur and can advise on areas where dormice should be taken into account when planning road developments. Planning law has now been strengthened so that any new development scheme that impacts on woods or hedgerows likely to contain hazel dormice must be preceded by a dormouse survey and appropriate steps must be taken to rescue the animals before they are obliterated. Focussing on dormice in this way also benefits many other species. But you can't protect animals if you don't know where they are, so these nut hunts have been very helpful in finding out.

It may take a dormouse 20 minutes or more to get into a ripe hazel nut.

Can we learn anything from distribution maps?

Why is the hazel dormouse found in some places and not others? If we could answer this question, we might get some clues as to why it has become rare and how we might act to save it dying out altogether. Perhaps the dormouse is limited by the distribution of a plant species vital to its survival? However, the three plants most commonly associated with it are hazel, honeysuckle and bramble. All are important to dormice, but all are widespread virtually throughout the British mainland. Clearly they are not responsible for limiting the distribution of *Muscardinus*. Nevertheless, comparison of various distribution maps might at least suggest some more ideas for useful research, in the absence of any other helpful information.

Studying the distribution of hazel dormice reveals a very distinctive pattern. The map shows a strong concentration of records in the south and west, with outliers in the north (Cumbria, Northumberland). The general picture is of scarcity or absence across a broad swathe of central England, running diagonally from Devon to the Wash. This corresponds remarkably with what Oliver Rackham called 'managed countryside'. Here, the ancient forest was cleared in the past, leaving open country. The few woods that exist there now are usually isolated and have often been planted in relatively modern times. It is likely that woodland clearance and open country are not good for dormice, even if the woods are replanted later. Local absence today may therefore reflect woodland management in the past. Conversely, Rackham's 'ancient countryside', characteristic of the Weald and also much of the south west, corresponds to the counties where dormice are most widespread and abundant. In these regions, the open countryside has been carved out of the ancient wildwood, much of which still remains. Copses and woods are still more or less continuous, being well linked by hedges and woodland strips. We might learn from this that woods are best if they retain links to other wooded sites and it is not good to isolate copses and woods from each other. Detailed studies on the ground have confirmed these suggestions and also

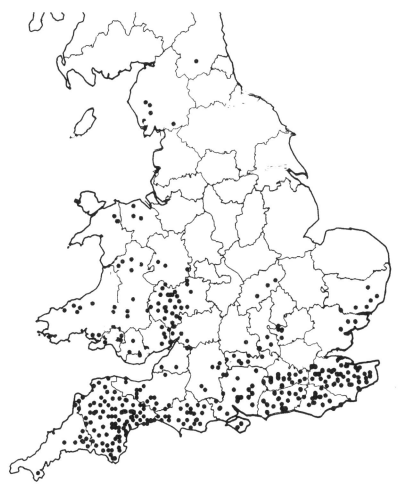

Distribution of the hazel dormouse. The dots are not meant to indicate actual sites, but simply to convey the general areas where these animals are most likely to be found. Recent introductions (e.g. to Cheshire and Yorkshire) have not been included.

that ancient semi-natural woodland is a good habitat for dormice.

The distribution of hazel dormice in Britain has four distinctive features. There are widespread and fairly numerous localities across the south from Kent to Devon. There is a northward extension through Herefordshire to south Shropshire. Dormice are present in Suffolk, but absent from Norfolk. There is a small cluster of dormouse sites in the southern Lake District and around Hexham in Northumberland. If other species show a similar pattern of distribution, they may provide hints as to what might have caused the decline of the dormouse and its present-day limitation to certain areas. It seemed like a good idea to browse through a selection of distribution maps for other animals. This revealed that the only other British small mammal with a similar distribution is the yellow-necked mouse. Like the dormouse, it is present in Suffolk, but not Norfolk, and largely absent from a broad area of central England. It is likely that some of the biological and historical factors responsible for limiting present-day distribution in the dormouse also affect yellow-necked mice, but unfortunately we don't know how. That line of enquiry seems like a blind alley, for the moment at least.

Looking at maps of the distribution of woodland birds revealed that the three that most closely match the distribution of the hazel dormouse are nuthatch, turtle dove and lesser spotted woodpecker. However, all three are common in Norfolk and the first two are also widespread in northern England where the dormouse is rare or absent. Little is learnt from this comparison. On the other hand, maps showing the decline of the wryneck and red backed shrike seem to be linked to climatic changes since the 1940s. Climate might also be important to the dormouse, a suggestion that became an important focus for some of our research and is considered later in this book.

As warm-blooded animals, dormice ought to be relatively unaffected by climatic factors, at least in comparison with reptiles and insects which depend a lot on warmth and sunshine. However, there are some striking parallels with butterflies, which are certainly highly sensitive to weather and climate. Butterfly species richness closely follows the pattern of dormouse distribution, with more than 30 species being present over most of its range (even highlighting a difference between Suffolk and Norfolk). This comparison also identifies a climatically favourable area of southern Cumbria with more butterfly species than for nearly 200 km to the south. Again this matches one of the distinctive features of dormouse distribution, that it is present in southern Cumbria, but absent from almost everywhere else in the north of England. This too points to the need to consider climate as a possible factor in dormouse distribution and decline.

There are actually five fairly abundant butterfly species that show strongly southern distributions like the dormouse. The maps for the brimstone and comma show the best match with the dormouse, but both these butterflies are widespread in both Suffolk and Norfolk. The speckled wood is frequent in many parts of Scotland where dormice do not occur. The white admiral is scarce in East Anglia and shares with the dormouse a corridor of sites northward into Hereford, but it is absent from Cumbria (and most of Wales and central England). The silver washed fritillary is also scarce in East Anglia, like the dormouse, but is rare in Kent where the dormouse is not. Far from being helpful, this is just confusing!

However, butterfly distributions are not static. For example, the white admiral spread as far north as Lincolnshire in the 1930s and 1940s, apparently reinvading areas where it had occurred in the last century. This seems to have been in response to climatic changes leading to warmer temperatures at a critical stage of its life cycle. Apparently, the comma was also once widespread, from Somerset to Cumbria. It had contracted by 1920 to a central area, then expanded again, reaching Yorkshire and Lancashire by 1950. Again the contraction and spread appear to result from climatic changes. But a key difference between butterflies and dormice is that the latter cannot fly. If adverse climatic change resulted in local extinctions of the dormouse, its national distribution would shrink irrevocably. This is exactly what seems to have happened over the last 100 years. Unlike the butterflies, its loss from many areas would be permanent because it is unable to redistribute itself by flying across an inhospitable landscape. So, gazing at maps may be confusing, but it is not a waste of time if it leads to useful ideas suggesting where research should be done.

Having had these pointers towards climate as a factor to investigate, I looked at this in more detail. Maps of climatic data show dormice prefer drier parts of Britain (but it's pretty wet where they occur in south Devon!). Temperature was clearly correlated with dormouse distribution too. Almost all the known dormouse sites occur where the average temperature of the warmest month (July) exceeds 16.5°C. The best match to the pattern of dormouse distribution was a map of sunshine hours. This even showed that there was less sunshine in Norfolk than in Suffolk and a sunny area north into Shropshire, just like the distribution of dormouse records. Although sunshine seems completely irrelevant to a nocturnal animal, it is in fact very important to the dormouse. It is sunshine that opens flowers and helps insects to grow, both essential foods for dormice. It also ripens the fruits and nuts on which they feed. So, indirectly sunshine is important after all. Sunny weather is also not rainy weather, and this is good too. Dormice are very sensitive to wet as their fine fur is not good at keeping dry.

A characteristic pose – sitting across a twig, balanced by the hanging tail.

These studies all point to climate as being a possible long-term factor affecting the history and decline of the dormouse, issues that are revisited elsewhere in this book. Meanwhile, a glance at the dormouse map, with its obvious emphasis on southern counties, suggests to many people that it cannot survive cold winters in the north. In fact this is wrong. Across Europe, hazel dormice manage very well in places where the winters are far more severe than in Britain. Cold winters are not an issue, but our variable and mild winters do cause problems, particularly in waking the animals unnecessarily during the hibernation period. Actually, it's not the winter that is the problem at all, it's the variable and often rotten weather we get when the dormice are active in summer!

Nesting and nest boxes

Hazel dormice make their own nests by weaving shredded honeysuckle bark or other fibrous material into a ball. A few leaves are built into a loose outer layer. These nests, about the size of a grapefruit, can sometimes be found in bramble bushes. In fact this is where they are most easily found and this has led to the belief that dormice normally make such nests and normally live in brambles. In fact they seem to use these nests mainly when they are feeding on bramble flowers or fruits. The rest of the time they appear to seek out a more weatherproof and secure nesting place. Our radio tracking shows that they often use available shelters provided by hollow trees (64% of nestings in one study) and the existing nests of squirrels or birds. Sometimes they go behind loose tree bark where rotting has left a space between the bark and the tree trunk. They seem to have little loyalty to one particular nest, and move house frequently.

But hazel dormice are also found accidentally from time to time in bird nest boxes. Knowing this, and in an inspired move, Doug Woods (a keen Somerset naturalist) designed some boxes specially for dormice. They were small, and had the entrance hole facing the tree trunk to make it easier for the dormice to enter. A spacing bar kept the front of the box away from the tree allowing room for the animals to squeeze into the entrance. Subsequently we had several thousand of these boxes made and they proved a vital tool for studying dormice. They also enabled people to see these beautiful but elusive creatures and show them to their children.

At one site in Cumbria, the first dormice nested in a box within 22 days of its being set up. As the attractiveness of nest boxes confirms, tree holes may be the principal natural nest sites used by dormice, not the nests they build for themselves as had been assumed previously. This is especially likely early and late in the summer when the weather is not so good and sparse foliage in the shrub layer would mean that nests built there would be rather exposed. Where nest boxes are put up (effectively providing artificial tree holes), almost the entire dormouse population may use them. In a radio tracking study we found that 85% of the 75 nests used by the dormice were in nest boxes.

A nest box in a loop of wire, with spacing bars to keep the entrance hole from being blocked by the tree.

We put up nest boxes at about 1.5 metres above the ground (shoulder height, where it is convenient to ourselves). A study of box use at different heights showed that this was actually the height preferred by dormice too. Boxes put up higher are no more attractive to dormice and are a nuisance to inspect as they need a ladder to reach them. Low boxes are vulnerable to predators. Once established, the nest boxes allow regular collection of data on breeding and body weights, for example, making it possible to study these aspects of dormouse biology for the first time. Before you can 'disturb' dormice by checking them in their nest boxes a licence is required (see page 142 for details). We did worry that frequent disturbance, especially regular monthly visits to collect data, might cause distress to the animals, so we performed an experiment. Disturbing the boxes in the normal way caused about a third of them to depart, but only as far as another box nearby. One third of the animals disappeared temporarily, but the remainder stayed in the same box and were still there next day. So disturbance seems not to be a problem. Certainly handling the animals gently does not cause obvious signs of distress and they normally do not even try to bite.

In coppiced areas and young shrubs, food may be abundant, but tree holes might be a limiting factor for dormice as young shrubs rarely have holes in them. It is in such habitats that nest boxes are most successful. In one of our studies, the numbers of dormice apparently doubled within months in response to putting up boxes, probably as a result of attracting dormice in and also a probably increased survival of juveniles. A comparable situation has been observed in pied flycatchers, in which a thirteen-fold increase in numbers was achieved in three years by providing nest boxes. At one of our study sites, there were 104 babies born in about 100 nest boxes a year after they were put up.

Inside the box, dormice will sometimes be found lying on the bare wood, but normally they weave a small domed nest, using shredded honeysuckle bark whenever it is available. Nest boxes within five metres of honeysuckle are more likely to be occupied by dormice than those sited away from this preferred nesting material. Often the nest will be topped off with a few fresh green hazel leaves gathered from the branches above. These domed nests are very distinctive; the wood mice that also use nest boxes normally only have a layer of brown dead leaves (collected off the ground), with no roof to the nest.

Dormice do not normally use nest boxes in winter, but seek out a cool place on the ground apparently to ensure a stable temperature at which to hibernate. Inside a nest box, winter temperatures may fall below freezing on a frosty night, but can easily get quite hot if the sun strikes the box on a warm day. Variable temperatures are not good

A dormouse nest made of layers of woven leaves and stripped honeysuckle bark.

for hibernators, so the dormice go somewhere else.

At the end of the year, after the dormice have gone, it is probably a good idea to empty out the boxes. This will remove old bird nests, many of which contain a lot of fur and can harbour mites and other potentially harmful parasites. Throwing out old nesting material also prevents the inside of the box being damp for long periods after winter rain. Dry boxes will last longer than those that stay damp and rot.

Competition for nest boxes

Birds like nest boxes too, especially blue tits and great tits. Often at least a third of our boxes are used by them in the spring. However, these two species have normally finished breeding before the dormice emerge fully from hibernation, so there isn't really much of a problem. Anyway, if a dormouse finds an attractive nest box with a batch of juicy eggs in it, they will be eaten. This doesn't really matter as tits are pretty common birds. A bigger problem occurs with pied flycatchers. These are quite rare and they also nest later, so their eggs are more likely to still be there when the dormice arrive. Loss of pied flycatcher clutches does upset the bird people.

Gordon Vaughan, an energetic ornithologist in Devon, thought of the brilliant idea of intercepting Welsh pied flycatchers as they migrated through his woods in spring and managed to get them nesting in substantial numbers, boosting the Devon population of this rare species. He was a bit cross when his flycatcher boxes were taken over by tits, but he put up extra ones to ensure that there would be some vacancies when the migrating flycatchers arrived later. These were used by nuthatches, so he put his boxes up in batches of three to satisfy all customers, only to have them used by dormice, who also ate the eggs of his birds! His frustration was vented in the bird literature, with complaints about 'dormousitis', a disease that was spreading to many English woods and threatened rare bird populations. However, the dormice were only a threat to his pied flycatchers because he put up the nest boxes in the first place. We have had an enjoyable and lengthy correspondence on this matter for many years, with a truce declared in 2003 when both bird and dormouse numbers appeared to have seriously declined, presumably due to some other causes such as the weather.

Other nest box inhabitants

Dormice aren't the only tenants of our nest boxes. Invaders include bank voles and pigmy shrews (rarely common shrews) and sometimes bats. Occasionally we get bumble bees, some species of which habitually go for old mammal nests apparently seeking them out by smell. Bee colonies make a huge and intimidating buzzing noise when the box is disturbed, although there are usually only a few of them present. Best left alone anyway. Orange underwing moths are also a common invader in the autumn, but like the bees they appear to be common at one or two sites and absent everywhere else. Slugs and other soil animals move in wherever the boxes are damp.

Food, habitat and ecological requirements of hazel dormice

The hazel dormouse has a simple digestive system like our own and cannot usefully exploit easily available foods such as leaves. Digesting these requires a more elaborate system, incorporating microbes to assist in digesting plant cellulose. The dormouse doesn't do this. Instead it is a selective feeder, concentrating on the most nutritious food sources available, namely flowers, fruits and insects. However, our radio tracking reveals that it also feeds only up in the trees and shrubs, where these foods are frequently limited by season and occur only in particular trees at any one time. The dormouse therefore needs habitat containing a lot of different types of shrubs and trees in order to ensure a continuous supply of food through the changing seasons.

It appears that the animals feed initially on flowers like hawthorn, selecting those that are at the right stage of ripeness. The stamens, with their packets of pollen, provide a nutritious food, particularly as the dormice reject the flowers that have been open too long and have lost most of their pollen due to wind and rain. After a couple of weeks or so, these flowers will be finished and the dormice move on to the next thing that becomes available. This may be honeysuckle, where they nibble at the sweet nectar-producing parts of the flower, or they may go for sycamore flowers. Bramble flowers are popular too, although the dormice may find it hard to travel far through the prickly bushes. In fact bramble is a very valuable feature of dormouse habitats because it produces flowers over a long period (sometimes up to six weeks) and then lots of berries in the autumn. Hazel dormice are especially fond of blackberries, and who can blame them?

Come the autumn, there is plenty of food around in the form of berries and they will go out of their way to visit any accessible yew trees to eat their juicy fruits. Beech and hazel nuts are taken too. The latter are especially important to dormice, who gnaw the ripe nuts when they are still green and before they fall to the ground. They appear not to eat acorns, perhaps because of the bitter-tasting tannins they contain and also because they are a bit large and slippery for a dormouse to

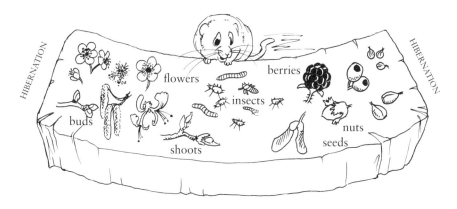

flowers

berries

buds

insects

shoots

nuts

seeds

A dormouse smörgasbord.

cope with. Dormice will eat the seeds out of ash keys and also the little seeds of hornbeams. These are too hard for most things to crack open, and too small to be worth squirrels wasting time gnawing at them. But dormice will nibble into them and get a useful meal. All this feeding activity goes on up in the branches of trees and shrubs. The dormice will not descend to the ground to eat, so they don't make use of the additional foods that might be found there.

This type of feeding means that the animals must move from one tree species to the next when each one makes some new flowers or fruits available as the season progresses. There is a bit of a problem in midsummer, when the flowers are mostly over but the fruits and nuts are not yet ripe. At this time they eat a lot of insects, especially the tiny caterpillars that devastate the leaves of oak and hazel. They also eat lots of aphids ('greenfly'). There may not be much meat on an aphid, but these tiny creatures are sweet tasting and occur in millions. They don't require much effort to catch. We have watched a dormouse scuttling about among leaves and twigs, hoovering up aphids from the underside of leaves as fast as it could. Dormice will eat insects whenever they can, and samples of their droppings will contain insect fragments (visible under the microscope) throughout the summer. Insects are such a useful food to dormice that trees harbouring plenty of them are a valuable asset in the habitat. The entomologists tell us that oaks support the most insect species, but dormice are more interested in quantity rather than insect types. We could find little information about which trees support the biggest tonnage of insects, so we asked a specialist entomologist to gas some trees and collect what fell out. She showed that oaks certainly had large quantities of insect food up in the canopy, but so did hazel and alder. Ash trees seemed to be the least useful insect suppliers, apart from rhododendrons which were almost useless as a food source.

Much of their food comes from bushes such as bramble and hazel, but the tall trees are also important for dormice as they frequently offer food resources at a different time to the shrubs below. Since dormice do not travel very far, yet need access to a variety of trees and shrubs, it follows that the best habitats will be those that contain many species of woody plants all mixed up. Such a situation is often found in ancient woodland, where the centuries have allowed plenty of time for a full range of species to develop. That doesn't mean to say that dormice do not occur elsewhere, simply that ancient woodlands are often good dormouse habitat. In fact dormice often thrive in scrub, like the hawthorn and hazel thickets that invade open hillsides when grazing animals are removed. Such shrubs get the full benefit of the sun and are highly productive of dormouse food. However, these habitats are often transient and after a few decades they become shaded woodland, with dormice becoming less abundant as time goes by.

Managed ancient woods are particularly good habitats because felling trees and coppicing hazels and sweet chestnuts mean the canopy is opened up and sunlight can enter the wood. This stimulates plenty of fresh growth, supports insects and flowers and generally enhances the food supply. Indeed shading, caused by lack of woodland management, seems to be one of the features that threatens survival and has resulted in loss of dormice from many places. Dense shade suppresses growth and dormouse food, so they do not like shaded areas, but prefer the edges of woods and forest clearings where the shrubs enjoy plenty of sunshine. The best dormouse woods are so shrubby that you can't see more than a metre or two in any direction once you leave a path. Woods that are so opened up by the effects of shading that you can see for 50 metres are rarely much use for dormice.

So, ancient, managed woods are good habitat, but woodland management, especially coppicing, is no longer economical. For centuries, cutting hazels at ground level ('coppicing') to get them

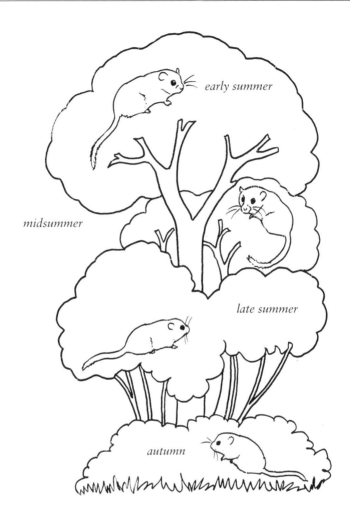

Principal areas for dormouse foraging: height from the ground related to season (a generalisation).

to grow new poles was the most valuable use of our woods. It provided thin poles for weaving into fences and for making wattle and daub houses. Bigger poles could be dried and burnt to make charcoal. The hazels would be cut every 5-20 years, depending on the size of poles wanted. This activity meant the wood was being constantly regenerated, maintaining good conditions for dormice. By the mid 20th century, we no longer used these traditional woodland products to any extent and this type of management ceased, especially in northern areas. No doubt that was another factor in causing dormice to die out in many woods. Nowadays, when conservation managers want to encourage coppicing (because it is good for birds, woodland flowers, butterflies and other insects), they need to be careful not to cut too much at once or there will be insufficient habitat left for the dormice. Moreover, hazels only start to produce nuts again after seven years, so it is important to make sure that the hazel is not cut too often. (See also problems with deer, page 73.)

Food quality and quantity are likely to be reduced in areas with poor soils. Good dormouse sites are usually on calcium-rich and neutral soils while acid and sandy soils often support poor dormouse habitat. The shape of the land may be relevant too because hilly places will have sunny and shaded slopes, varying the time at which flowers and fruits will be available. It is surely no coincidence that many of the best areas for dormice are in areas of slopes and valleys, while flat or undulating country offers less potential.

The physical structure of a wood is also important. Where trees have all grown at the same time, colonising open ground for example, they tend to become very tall and spindly as they all compete with each other to reach the sunlight. Such woods are poor habitat for dormice because the heavy shade under the trees supports few flowering and fruiting shrubs. Hazels and hawthorns might still grow there, but they are no longer vigorous enough to provide nuts or berries. The spindly trees have few side branches, making it difficult for the dormice to move through the wood above ground level. The tree canopies are also spindly and very unstable even in a gentle breeze. Such woods need to be opened out, with substantial tree clearance before they will support a good dormouse population, management which will benefit many other plants and animals too.

Sycamores

Conservationists hate sycamores because they are not native to Britain and their broad leaves cast a dense shade, making it hard for many other types of flowers and shrubs to grow underneath. But sycamores can be useful to dormice, providing them with plenty of flowers in early summer. Later, the leaves support vast numbers of aphids, another valuable food for dormice. In fact there are some places where dormice have been able to colonise strips of woodland that are formed almost wholly of fast growing sycamores. However, this is probably only a temporary success. Sooner or later the sycamores will shade out the other vegetation and dormice probably cannot live on sycamore alone. Moreover, sycamore helicopters spread the seedlings widely, and soon these trees dominate everything. So, a few sycamores may be good, but lots of them aren't. A compromise is to have a few sycamores that are coppiced every few years so they support lots of aphids on their fresh young leaves, but never get old enough to produce their winged seeds, nor tall enough to cast a widespread shade.

Conifers

Dormice seem to like a varied range of tree species, so conifer plantations would appear to be hopeless habitat. Yet people often find dormice in such places. Sometimes this is because the animals actually live in the fringe of bushes outside the plantation, but they may also use the conifers themselves. Some species carry large numbers of aphids that would form useful dormouse food. They also exude resin and maybe the dormice actually eat that? Elsewhere in the world, possums, lemurs and marmosets exploit sap and resins as a food source. If dormice did too, then this would enable them to survive in conifers better than we might expect. In fact, edible dormice also gnaw at conifers and seem to use the sticky sap as food, so perhaps Muscardinus does too? Maybe a few conifers could be valuable additions to the habitat, and should not all be removed where they have been planted in deciduous woodland. They also provide shelter from the wind. However, too many will surely be bad because of the shade they cast, at the expense of other trees and shrubs.

Dormice in hedges

Some hedges, particularly ancient ones, may have a wide range of shrubby species. These provide plenty of dormouse food and also benefit from the absence of big trees casting shade over them. Hedges can be long strips of ideal dormouse habitat and the animals may live there permanently. At other times they may simply use hedges as a sheltered dispersal route, enabling them to cross otherwise open ground between patches of woodland. Hedges that are cut frequently will have most of their flowers and berries removed, reducing their value to dormice. The best hedges are straggly ones, at least 3-4 metres wide, near to woods and with plenty of different shrubs within. Heavy management of hedges, particularly annual flailing to cut the tops and sides, has resulted in the loss of dormice from many hedges where they were found not so long ago. It is better to cut hedges one side this year and the other a couple of years later. As dormice do not like to travel on the ground, particularly in long wet grass, they will turn back from large gaps in hedges. Gaps mean that a hedgerow no longer forms a good corridor to assist movements between small copses. Fortunately, farmers can get grants (under countryside stewardship schemes) to help plant hazels and hawthorns to fill these gaps, and they no longer receive government subsidies for wholesale hedgerow destruction in the name of farming efficiency. This is good news for dormice.

Dormice are fond of blackberries, and who can blame them?

Follow that dormouse!

Trying to watch wild dormice at night is a pretty hopeless activity. They operate high in the trees and often hide behind leaves and branches. Even large squirrels can be difficult to see when they do this, and dormice do it in the dark! Using a red torch makes little difference. Direct observations are hard to make and the animals soon scoot off through the branches where they cannot be followed. The only way to see where they go and find out what they do is to use radio tracking. This has been done before in studies of ordinary mice, but these stay mostly on the ground. Radio tracking has been done for squirrels active up in the trees, but in daylight. Nobody had previously tried radio tracking tiny dormice, which are active up trees and in the dark. The radio transmitters have to be very small too, about the size of a pea, so they have only a short range and brief life.

Nevertheless, once a dormouse has been fitted with a radio collar, its movements can be followed using a special direction-finding receiver. This is still not the end of the problems, because the slightest noise or snagging of the big receiver antenna on a twig will result in the animal you are following disappearing at high speed somewhere else. It may take ages to find it again. Even when you can locate where a dormouse is, high above you in a tree, you may not know exactly where you are yourself, especially in the dark and in the dense undergrowth favoured by dormice. Nowadays this problem can be solved using a GPS device that tells you exactly where you are, although sometimes inaccurately under dense foliage. During our early studies, the GPS system received deliberate and random interference because the Americans feared terrorists might use it to guide weapons to sensitive targets. So we had to find another way of locating ourselves accurately (to the nearest few metres), in the dark, in order to map dormouse movements precisely.

We did this by laying out long parallel wires through the study site. The wires were five metres apart and had numbered tags attached at five metre intervals. After locating a dormouse, it was necessary to crawl to the nearest wire, crawl along it to the first tag and from that work out where you had been. The position could then be recorded as grid coordinates (like latitude and longitude) for entry into a computer. This immensely challenging procedure had to be repeated at several of our study sites, one of which required some six kilometres of wires to be laid out before radio tracking could begin (and removed again a few weeks later). The expense and sheer practical difficulty of radio tracking dormice is one reason why we have information from only a limited range of study sites and habitats.

Analysing the dormouse movement data showed they rarely moved more than about 60-80 metres from their nests, males being more wide ranging than females. By contrast, wood mice may go half a kilometre from home. Dormice usually travel less than 150 metres in a whole night. Their total home range area (the space they use during normal activity) is probably only about one hectare in an entire season, with many parts of this area not being used. In practice, dormice tend to focus activity on small patches within their home range, exploiting the food there while it lasts, then moving on to use a different part of their range for a week or two. Males have

Wrens also make spherical nests, but with a distinct entrance hole and few leaves, if any.

Males may display aggressively towards each other, just as squirrrels do in daytime.

larger ranges than females. By travelling about more, males can meet up with several females whose ranges they overlap. However, they are territorial and males seem to use their ranges as exclusive territory, not overlapping with the area used by neighbouring males. Occasionally rival males can be seen by red torchlight facing up to each other at their territory boundaries, flicking their tails aggressively just as squirrels do. Aggressive encounters are also observed in captivity. Other evidence of territoriality includes finding a constant density of males, but variable numbers of females. Moreover, males do not share the same nest in the breeding season, but females will. Spacing the animals out by territorial defence limits the population density and consequent pressure on food supplies, but it also means that small woods may have too few dormice to keep the population going.

Radio tracking also revealed that over 70% of the natural nests (i.e. excluding nest boxes) that the animals used in one study were more than three metres above the ground. Up there they would not be found by normal human searchers, so dormice could be present but easily overlooked. In the past, naturalists had been convinced that the nests they found low down in brambles and shrubs were the preferred and normal nesting places. But they aren't; such nests are simply the ones most easily and most commonly found by humans who cannot easily search more then two metres off the ground. Other natural nest sites include disused squirrel dreys and bird nests, hollow branches, gaps behind tree bark and within tangled ivy and honeysuckle. Where nest boxes are provided, these are the preferred nesting places. They seem to build their own nests rather infrequently.

Dormice are entirely arboreal, feeding in the canopy of trees or shrubs. Getting to their food requires agility, small body size and appropriate adaptations such as gripping paws and highly flexible ankles. The dormouse must also be familiar with the exact details of its three-dimensional habitat in order to travel to feeding places. It must know precise routes, branch by branch, otherwise much time will be wasted moving along branches whose tips bear no food or do not link to the next tree. Perhaps the size of the animal's home range is limited by its ability to remember complex three-dimensional routes that have to be followed very precisely, in the dark.

Senses

Dormice cannot distinguish between colours after dark, and probably not during the daytime either. In fact their eyesight is not very good, despite their large eyes. Smell is far more important to them, both for locating suitable foods and for inspecting them to ensure they are ripe enough to eat.

We were once given a dormouse that had travelled across sheep pasture, apparently attracted by a huge wall of flowering honeysuckle over 400 metres from the wood where it normally lived. Dormice also have an acute sense of hearing, which makes it very difficult to creep up on them at night.

Social behaviour

It's hard to know what dormice get up to in the dark, but various bits of evidence and occasional direct observations do provide some clues. There are whimsical accounts in some of the old natural history books suggesting that dormice live in colonies and are sociable creatures. This might be based on finding families of well grown young still living with their mothers. In fact, even in areas of relatively uniform habitat, dormice are often patchily distributed, as though they live in social groups, perhaps extended families. The occurrence of up to seven well grown animals in the same nest box also suggests there may be a social dimension to dormouse behaviour. They might know each other and choose to live together, even if it's only to keep each other warm in bad weather. Up to 65% of adult male dormice have been found living in a nest box with one or more females.

This cohabitation occurs mainly outside the periods when young are born. We also found a few cases where the same male and female had been found together in a nest box two years running, having come back together after hibernation. Similar behaviour has been reported from several sites on the Continent, suggesting dormice might form long-term pair bonds. This is often found among monkeys and some carnivores, but is unexpected in a small rodent species, most of which do not live long enough to make it worth 'getting married'!

Torpor: opting out of the British summer

Faced with nasty weather, particularly in early summer, the response of the dormouse is to give up and resign from the game. It stays in the nest and becomes torpid. The body cools down and the animal appears to be in hibernation, even in June or July. Often at this time, particularly in the morning, inspecting nest boxes will find the majority of dormice cold, inactive and completely incapable of making more than slow creaky movements. They may make quiet wheezing noises, but take at least ten minutes to warm up sufficiently to crawl about. Later in the day, when the air temperature may be higher, the torpid animals seem to wake up of their own accord ready for a night's activity as soon as it gets dark. Temperature recorders in the nest boxes reveal that in early summer dormice may spend eight hours or more each day in this torpid condition.

It looks as though the dormouse can switch off its physiology, and abandon its normal warm blooded state. Maintaining a high body temperature costs a lot of energy, especially for small animals, in which heat loss is more rapid than in larger ones. Consequently, going torpid economises on energy costs. This is very important in early summer when there is often not much food about. The dormouse is in danger of going out to feed, using up a lot of energy in moving about and keeping itself warm, but getting little back from the small amounts of food that it manages to find. The colder or wetter the weather is, the greater the danger of an energy deficit. Entering torpor for part of the day probably saves about 20% of daily energy expenditure (rather like turning off the central heating when we go to bed).

By the autumn, when there is plenty of food about in the form of nuts and berries, dormice spend only a small amount of time in torpor or none at all. Whilst torpor is an obvious and efficient response to the problem of balancing the dormouse's energy budget during times when the weather is bad or food is scarce, torpor does have its drawbacks. Going torpid in the breeding season is not such a good idea!

The dormouse characteristically breeds late, often more than three

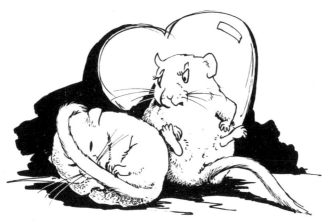

Their wild night was ruined as torpor overcame him.

months after other small mammals. Perhaps this is why. The individuals save themselves from starving by reducing energy expenditure when food is short, but this inevitably then means that they cannot produce their first litters until later than other mammals whose feeding habits do not impose such limitations on their activities. In turn, this means that dormice are unlikely to have time to raise a second litter that year, reducing the potential rate of population increase and helping to keep dormice rare. In effect the adult animals escape starvation, but at the expense of the size of the next generation. No other British mammals seem to use summer torpor as part of their normal lives, except the bats. Like dormice, they are very sensitive to temperature and the flying insects on which they feed are scarce and hard to catch in cold, windy or rainy conditions. In this respect, dormice have more in common with bats than with squirrels or ordinary mice. It is quite likely that in countries where the summers are warmer and/or drier than in Britain, torpor is less frequently necessary and breeding success is consequently greater.

The dormouse spends eight to ten hours per day in torpor for at least part of the summer. In addition, it might spend another eight hours each day in normal sleep, and then it hibernates almost continuously for five monthsor more over winter. This means that it spends over three quarters ofits life asleep! Maybe it is a measure of consummate success, that the animal can do all it needs to by way of breeding and growing up, all in a tiny fraction of the time that other species devote to normal life. Maybe being asleep is the pinnacle of ecological and evolutionary achievement? But then when I try to apply this logic to some of my dozy students I know it cannot be true.

A sleepy name

The dormouse is a sleepy creature and this has been known for centuries. Indeed its very name 'dormouse' has a similar structure to other sleep-associated words like 'dormant' and 'dormitory', perhaps derived from the French word 'dormir' meaning to sleep.

Its old English name was 'sleeper' and Lewis Carroll had his dormouse fall asleep constantly at the Mad Hatter's tea party, one of the many zoologically accurate observations that he built into the tales of Alice in Wonderland.

The dormouse falls asleep at the Mad Hatter's tea party (illustration by Tenniel from Alice in Wonderland*).*

Breeding, numbers and lifespans

Dormice are usually born late in the season, in July or August. It is rare to find babies as early as June. This is several weeks after other small rodents have already raised at least one family. The commonest family size is about four, but sometimes more than eight babies can be found together. This might represent exceptionally large litters, but it could also be where two females have combined their babies into a crèche. In a couple of cases, the babies have been of two clearly different size groups, suggesting the latter is likely. If mothers do share the job of raising young, then this adds to the evidence for a social dimension to the life of dormice that is unexpected among small mammals. It is also true that dormouse babies, being few in number, are 'precious'. This is perhaps why females might help each other to raise them and also why mothers rarely seem to eat or desert their young if they are disturbed, unlike rabbits or mice whose babies are produced in much larger numbers and often get eaten or deserted in times of stress.

It takes between six and eight weeks to wean a litter; the young appear to remain with their mother for an unusually long period. It seems that they join her on foraging trips, learning the way about their complex environment and returning to spend the day with her in the maternal nest. By breeding late and taking a long time to rear their young, females really have little chance of successfully raising more than one litter in a year, at least in Britain, although in captivity they can manage two or even three. By contrast, wild wood mice have up to six litters in a year. If dormice did produce second litters in the wild, they would not be born before late August and by the time they were weaned there would be little opportunity to fatten up before the oncoming winter. Early winters are likely to result in high mortality among late-born young because those that fail to reach about 12-15 g before hibernating are unlikely to survive. As a result of all this, the annual recruitment to dormouse populations is likely to be very low, perhaps only one or two surviving young per female. This is likely to vary widely according to the weather, and a high variation in annual recruitment rates is one of the most dangerous threats to small populations, leading swiftly to what is called an 'extinction vortex'. This is where insufficient new animals are recruited to the population, so there are fewer animals to breed next year and, as a result, fewer still the year after and so on until the population fizzles out. In some other countries a longer breeding season is possible and two litters may be more normal. Survival is higher and dormouse populations are probably more secure.

Dormice live at a much lower population density than other woodland small mammals like wood mice and bank voles. Typically there are only 5-10 adult dormice per hectare, even in the best habitats, whereas mice and voles are often ten times more abundant. This means that small isolated woodlands have small dormouse populations that are highly vulnerable to chance events. For example, a five-hectare wood might have 30-50 dormice, half of them females. But chance alone (too many males born one year for example) could easily cause only 10-15 to be females, too few to ensure survival of the population, especially if the next generation suffers a similar excess of males or there is a poor survival rate due to the chance effects of bad weather. Computer modelling suggests that a dormouse population of 20 has a 50% chance of early extinction, simply due to such instability, irrespective of other factors such as predators or habitat changes.

Low population densities also mean that if a nature reserve of 30 hectares (74 acres) has only 5% of its area coppiced annually, after seven years (the time it takes for hazel to once again bear fruit), the remaining 19.5 hectares (50 acres) may be too small an area to support enough dormice to keep the population going. Many woodland reserves are considerably smaller than this, making the problem worse. Fragmentation of larger woods, by building roads for example, will have a similar effect. Small populations are also potentially threatened by the effects of inbreeding and the resulting lack of genetic diversity might limit the ability of dormice to cope with environmental challenges, including infectious diseases.

In compensation for a low recruitment rate, dormice appear to live a long time. Surprising numbers survive for five years or more, whereas other woodland rodents are lucky to survive five months. The life strategy of the dormouse seems to be based upon a low reproductive rate, balanced by living a long time. This is a lifestyle more normally associated with much larger animals. It contrasts with mice and voles in which large numbers of offspring are produced each year, but few survive very long. Both types of life strategy are adequate, but slower reproducing animals (like dormice) are more vulnerable to rapid change and to small population sizes simply because they lack the ability to compensate for losses by building up numbers quickly. This is also why tigers or eagles are more at risk of dying out than say rabbits or blue tits. Longevity may also be partly due to spending so much time inactive, safe from predators and not wearing the body out.

It seems that the dormouse is naturally rare, perhaps avoiding pressure on limited food supplies. Its small numbers and slow breeding enable it to survive perfectly well under normal conditions, but it is ill-equipped to respond to the rapid changes over large areas that are often caused by modern human activities.

Parasites

Dormice rarely have any fleas or ticks in their fur, although both are common on other small mammals. Sometimes they have mites that cause fur loss, but otherwise parasites are rare on dormice. However, one sad episode involved a small nematode worm that lives in damp leaf litter. These invaded some nest boxes that had not been cleaned out and were very damp inside. Some of the dormice then became infected by these tiny worms, which can also live as parasites. They wriggled their way into the eyes of the dormice, causing them to weep gently. The tears and mucus then dried, gumming the eyelids closed and preventing the animals from seeing. Several must have died before we discovered the problem and cleaned up the dormice. There has been no repeat of this distressing condition.

Predators

Weasels might get the occasional dormouse, particularly if any of them learned to raid nest boxes. Fortunately we have had only one case of this happening. Dormice form less than one in a thousand of the prey items taken by owls. This is probably because most British owls hunt mainly over grassland, taking principally field voles, and also because an owl would be wary of dashing into the dense twiggy branches where dormice live in case they damaged their big eyes. Barn owls cruising along farm hedgerows occasionally seize an unwary dormouse, but the most likely bird predator is the tawny owl. This species normally inhabits woodlands rather than open habitats, but it feeds mainly by watching from a perch and then dropping to the ground to snatch mice and voles. So long as dormice stay off the ground, they are probably fairly safe. However, video film of caged dormice in a wood showed at least two attacks on the animals by tawny and little owls. In other countries, where dormice may be more abundant, they turn up in owl pellets more frequently. In parts of Europe Tengmalm's owl is an extra potential predator.

Hibernation

In Britain dormice spend about half the year in hibernation, from October until May. During this time they are inactive and on the ground, in complete contrast to the summer season. This change in behaviour occurs about the time of the first frosts in the autumn and is brought about by the need to save energy at a time of year when food is not available in the usual places. To support their continued survival, the animals rely upon fat reserves accumulated during the previous autumn when food was abundant. Like hibernating bats of similar size, during the winter dormice consume fat reserves equivalent to about a quarter of their pre-hibernation body weight. This means that British Muscardinus need to weigh at least 12-15 g before hibernation in order to be fat enough to survive the winter. Checking nest boxes in spring confirms that the smaller ones are simply not there the following year. Adult dormice often hibernate at body weights greater than 30 g, having put on weight at a remarkable speed during the autumn. Sometimes their weight doubles in less than a month, especially when the weather is fine and there are plenty of nuts available in the trees.

In the past dormice have been reported to use tree stumps or leaf-filled coppice stools in which to hibernate, but these might simply be where people find them most often, not where the animals actually prefer to go. Radio tracking dormice in the autumn has revealed that some do use such places, but most simply nest under moss or loose leaf litter on the woodland floor. They make a tightly woven fibrous nest, about the size of a tennis ball, on the surface of the ground or in a small depression. Suitable places are probably available in most woodlands and are unlikely to be a limiting factor, but on the ground the hibernating animals become very vulnerable to floods, trampling and predation. The ancient rights of pannage (allowing commoners to give free range to their pigs in the autumn to feed on fallen nuts and berries) may well have eliminated dormice from many small woodlands. Even the odd pheasant has been seen to eat a hibernating dormouse that it found whilst scratching about on the ground.

It may seem pretty daft to hibernate in such vulnerable places, but

Hazel dormice normally hibernate alone.

there are significant advantages to hibernating on or under the ground. In particular, the air here is always moist, reducing water loss by the hibernating animals. If they used drier places, the dormice would need to wake up and drink in order to avoid becoming dangerously dehydrated. Waking up reduces fat reserves and increases the risk of predation if the animals come out into the open. Another advantage of hibernating on the ground is that the temperature there is low and fairly constant. The most efficient temperature at which to hibernate, where least energy is consumed in the form of stored fat, is probably between 1°C and 4°C. This is exactly what is normally found in the leaf litter and upper levels of the soil where dormice spend the winter. Maybe they could not hibernate for so long, because their fat would be used up sooner, if they chose somewhere that was safer, but also warmer. Like other hibernators, the dormouse allows its body temperature to fall to match that of the surroundings. This saves the energy cost of being warm blooded in an increasingly cold environment, although the metabolic rate will be raised to maintain the body above harmful freezing temperatures. Severe cold is therefore not the hazard that people often suppose.

If a hibernator is warmed, but not enough to wake up, its fat reserves

Dormice roll up tightly for hibernation and spend the winter in tighly woven nests under leaf litter, on the ground.

will be depleted faster by a raised metabolic rate and may be exhausted before the end of winter (especially if winter is unusually long). Higher winter temperatures could be compensated for by achieving higher body weights before hibernation, but that would mean feeding for longer in the autumn. Often this is not possible because frosts cause all the food to drop out of the trees, and this may happen very early in some years. An unpredictable climate, where the length and warmth of winter varies, poses severe problems for hibernators, yet highly variable seasons are a feature of the maritime climate in Britain. Hibernation is a strategy better suited to the relatively predictable (although more extreme) climates of Continental Europe, and dormice seem to be more secure there.

Under natural conditions, warming and arousal are normal in all hibernators. From time to time, hibernating dormice wake up during the day (not at dusk as in the summer) suggesting that arousal is prompted by daytime warmth. At a ground temperature of 9°C, arousal is more than twice as likely as at 3°C, and varying temperatures are even more likely to stimulate arousal. Sunny days may therefore be expected to cause dormice to wake up more often. But arousals mean that fat has to be used up in order to raise the body temperature to a normal level. Each arousal therefore consumes precious fat reserves that cannot be replaced in mid winter as natural foods have all gone from the trees. Warm days in early spring might be less of a problem if some sort of food (such as early catkins) is available, but arousal rarely results in a dormouse leaving its hibernation nest. Mostly it will just drop back into low-temperature torpor again within a few hours without going outside. Many stay in their winter nests for months at a time.

Hibernation is a strategy to overcome the problem posed by lack of food in the winter, but it subjects the dormouse to significant physiological challenges. Longer winters, higher and variable temperatures all add to the problems. When fat reserves are used up faster dormouse survival will be less likely, especially among small individuals. It is likely that these effects result in poorer survival in the north of England compared to the south, and in the west compared to the east. Although habitats are better in the west, the climate is not so good.

The dormouse hibernates on the ground, not in nest boxes. It selects a cool damp place where the temperature will remain constant throughout the winter. Underneath log piles and thick mats of moss are favourite sites, but it also retreats into dark tree stumps and under

Help a hibernator

Nest boxes have helped provide secure resting places for dormice in summer and it should be possible to help support them in winter. Hibernating on the ground makes dormice vulnerable to trampling. Putting out old clay flowerpots or roof ridge tiles might allow them to hibernate inside, safe from being trod upon. Porous clay tiles and pots are best because they do not create condensation. Instead they remain damp (good for hibernators) and evaporating moisture will also keep them cool.

brushwood. Sometimes it will just build its woven hibernation nest under a thick layer of fallen leaves, perhaps in a slight depression in the surface of the soil. Dormice often used to be found by woodmen cutting hazel coppice: the tiny woven nests would be found in the masses of dead leaves that accumulate in the base of hazel stools. Similarly, hedge cutting in winter often turned up hibernating dormice among the roots and tangled wood at the base of old hedges. A moist site is preferable to prevent the animal from drying out over winter (when it cannot easily replenish water lost through respiration) and a low temperature slows the rate at which the animal's metabolism will use up the reserves of stored fat. The ideal is probably about 4-5°C.

Dormice and the weather

The dormouse distribution map shows a strong southerly aspect, immediately suggesting some sort of climatic influence. Whenever people see a distribution map that shows a concentration in the south, for some reason they usually jump to the conclusion that this is a result of harsh winters. Perhaps the dormouse is limited to southern counties because it cannot cope with winter weather in the north?

In fact this is quite wrong. The distribution of the hazel dormouse in western Europe extends to southern Sweden, far further north than it occurs in Britain. It is also found widely in eastern Europe, including Poland, where the winters are far colder than here. Paradoxically, hibernating mammals are better off in cold winters. This is because the body temperature falls to match that of the surroundings. If the temperature drops below about 3°C, a hibernator's metabolism speeds up sufficiently to keep it from freezing, burning up some of the stored fat. Otherwise the cooler it is the longer its fat reserves will last because of a basic law of physical chemistry. This dictates that the rate at which all chemical reactions work (including physiological ones inside the body) doubles for every 10°C rise in temperature. So, at 15°C, an animal's metabolism is double the rate at 5°C, burning up fat stores twice as fast. But if it woke, there would be no food about for the dormouse to recharge its batteries.

So warm winters are the problem, not cold ones. Worse still are winters that are a bit of both hot and cold, leading to frequent arousals, with additional fat being used up. In warm and changeable winter weather, younger and less fat animals in hibernation may well run out of fuel long before spring comes and they will die without ever waking up for the summer.

However, the problem with the British climate is mainly in summer when the dormice are active and unusually sensitive. The fur of the dormouse is very fine and mostly lacks the water repellent guard hairs that are normal in other small mammals. These cause rain to run off the fur, but not in dormice whose coats can easily become waterlogged. Rain, mist or wet foliage is likely to result in soggy fur and consequent loss of body heat. Our radio tracking studies show that the effects of this are dramatic. Rainfall soon curtails activity and the animals quickly return to their nests, even if they have not had time to feed properly that night. Muscardinus is also very sensitive to temperature. Summer activity begins earlier on warm nights and continues for longer, leading to an average of 6.2 minutes extra activity per night for every degree Celsius rise in temperature. By the autumn the effect is doubled to more than 13 minutes per °C. Conversely, cold weather shortens activity and temperatures below 9°C at midnight seem to force the animals to become active in daylight, atypical behaviour which increases their vulnerability to predators.

As well as being directly sensitive to the weather, the dormouse is also indirectly affected, as a result of its specialised feeding ecology. Temperature and cloud cover will determine the availability of the flowers, insects and fruits upon which the dormouse feeds. Sunshine will affect ripening of fruits too. Flower development may well be delayed especially on northerly slopes, where sunshine is lacking or dissipated. Nectar is another dormouse food and its production is also closely linked to both sunshine and temperature. Perhaps it is not a surprise to find that the distribution map showing numbers of hours of sunshine for different parts of Britain bears a striking similarity to the distribution of the dormouse. At first sight this seems highly unlikely; why should a nocturnal animal be affected by hours of sunshine? However, once the peculiar feeding ecology of the dormouse is taken into account, dictated by its intestinal anatomy, the link becomes more obvious.

The other side of this coin is that cloudiness can be a problem because it reduces the effect of sunshine. Cloudiness increases with altitude and with dismal 'westerly' weather. Even quite a thin layer of cloud sharply reduces radiant heat from the sun and the amount that it can warm the fruits, flowers and insects, thereby speeding their development. We might then expect that dormice would be less successful at higher latitudes and further north in the country, where it is not only cooler, but also usually cloudier too. This seems to be the case and it is the higher and more northerly places from which dormice have disappeared first.

Dormouse distribution does not correspond very closely to maps of wind speeds, but this is probably because winds are normally measured at exposed sites, not in woodlands where dormice live. Even a slight breeze causes thin branches to move, and this must cause problems for dormice active up in the trees at night, especially if frequent stops become necessary in order to regain balance or wait for branches to stop moving before leaping between them. Winds could also exacerbate the effects of low temperature through the 'wind chill factor', which makes moving air feel colder than still air. Wind, rain, cold, whatever it is, shortening the activity period of the dormouse will make it that much less able to survive. The best places are south-facing, sun-warmed slopes and sheltered valleys, especially in the south-east, where rainfall is less than elsewhere.

Dormice, weather and climate change

The difference between weather and climate is that weather is what the dormouse has to put up with every day. Climate is the overall pattern of weather factors, the combination of sunshine, temperatures, rainfall etc. over longer periods of time. The weather will affect what dormice do on an hourly or daily basis. The climate dictates, over time, where they can and cannot live, effectively determining their geographical distribution and ultimately their fate as a British species.

The weather has a major influence on the activity patterns and foraging efficiency of the dormouse on a night-to-night basis. Climate may shorten the summer or influence food supplies. For example, the abundance and quality of beechnuts is determined by temperature, rainfall and sunshine during the whole summer. Dormice

eat beech mast and climatic factors may therefore affect the success of these animals through similar effects on their other food plants, such as the ripening of blackberries and the abundance and food value of hazel nuts.

Since dormice feed extensively on flowers, they are also likely to be very sensitive to the timing of flowering and fruiting, The average dates when flowers first open are later by about one day for every 30 m increase in altitude above sea level and for every 30 km further north you travel in Britain. A species like hawthorn or sycamore (useful dormouse foods), begins to flower about three weeks later in Scotland than in the south of England, and later still up in the hills. In years when winter begins early, the summer season will be shortened by a month or more in northern areas, perhaps leaving it too short to raise a successful family.

So, here is an animal that likes nice weather. Bad weather reduces activity and induces torpor; both are likely to reduce breeding success. The dormouse is also sensitive to weather conditions indirectly through its food. Thus long-term climate may define the ecological envelope within which the dormouse can exist. It is likely to be rarer and also more vulnerable at higher altitudes and towards the north. Predicted climate changes will therefore obviously have an effect on this species. However, much depends on what those changes turn out to be. If we get warmer summers, that may be good, but not if accompanied by more clouds and rain. Longer summers might be good too, as more second litters might survive, but more stormy autumn weather will certainly compromise feeding and fattening up for the winter. Much depends on what actual changes occur.

Meanwhile, the dormouse's distribution centres on those parts of England that are warm and dry in summer, with dry bright weather in winter. This is exactly where most of us would prefer to live too and there is a striking correspondence between dormouse distribution and the level of house prices!

Sunshine is good for dormice, even though they normally only come out at night.

The threat posed by Britain's unpredictable climate

Dormouse survival and breeding success are affected by the weather, but in Britain this is notoriously unpredictable. Winters may be cold, with heavy frosts or have several weeks of snow lying about. Other years, there might be no snow at all and people sunbathing in February. Summers can be wet or cold, sometimes both at once. Dormice cannot know in advance what the weather is going to be like. So each year they face uncertainty. If summer starts late, breeding will be delayed and fewer young can be reared before the next winter. If summer ends early, there will be less time in which to fatten up for hibernation. If they cannot feed adequately the younger animals will have insufficient fat reserves and their survival prospects will be poor.

Summer begins when certain flowers open, but this happy event can often vary by as much as six weeks from one year to another. The first flowering date for hazel, a key species for the dormouse, can vary by 50 days from one year to another. We could say that summer ends with the first frost. This is a key event for dormice because frosts kill off insects and cause remaining leaves and fruits to drop off the trees, effectively putting an end to feeding in the trees for that year. Between 1892 and 1984, the date of the first frost at Greenwich Observatory varied from October to late December, a range of over 100 days. Some summers could therefore be at least two months longer than others, long enough to raise another family. In other years it might be difficult for even one litter of young to grow big enough before being overtaken by winter.

In practice, everyone knows that the British summer is of unpredictable length and likely to occur sometime between April and December. Unpredictability on this scale must be a severe challenge to a weather and flower/ fruit/ insect dependent species like the dormouse. Over the long term, year-to-year variability becomes a significant factor in survival (or extinction) of whole populations. There will be 'good years', (with high recruitment and survival of young, low winter mortality) and 'bad years', with a reduction in population size because more die than survive. Small populations are disproportionately vulnerable to these ups and downs and many small local populations of dormice have become extinct as a result.

If there is a 'bad' year when few young survive, adult dormice can survive long enough to breed again if conditions are better the following year. However, in the highly variable British climate, one 'bad' year may well be followed by another. Three successive bad years would exceed the average dormouse lifespan and five bad years in a row is longer than the normal maximum age for this species in the wild. A run of bad years is therefore highly dangerous to small dormouse populations. Data from the weathermen reveal that the years 1910-1930 had consistently cold summers and warm winters. This combination is bad for dormice and that period coincides with a time when dormouse distribution declined significantly. Later records of summer sunshine reveal that the period 1960-1975 experienced only four 'good' years and there were five bad years in a row in the 1960s.

However, the dormouse responds to a combination of factors, not just sunshine or temperature. We need a more scientific way of assessing what constitutes a 'good' or 'bad' year for this species, based on how the weathermen classify weather patterns They talk about 'anticyclonic weather', which corresponds to 'good' conditions for dormice, being mainly dry, sunny and warm in summer and with cold dry weather in winter. 'Westerly weather' is the exact opposite, definitely bad for dormice. It is characterised by unsettled, miserable wet and cool conditions in summer, with dreary, mild weather in winter. Bad years would be ones where westerly weather patterns cropped up more often than the long-term average. In the period between 1861 and 1969, we had three bad years in a row five times. There was a run of four bad years after 1910 and several periods that suffered four bad years out of five. This must have resulted in the extinction of many dormouse populations, where there were too few animals left to recover their numbers before being hit again by bad weather. Westerly conditions are more frequent in the northern parts of Britain, which of course is where the hazel dormouse has died out in the last one hundred years.

Competition from squirrels and deer

It is possible that dormice suffer as a result of competition with squirrels for food, particularly hazel nuts, the main food the dormouse uses to fatten up for successful winter hibernation. At first sight this would seem not to be a problem. After all, dormice have successfully co-existed with our native red squirrels since the end of the last Ice Age. However, this species normally lives at far lower population densities than the introduced American grey squirrel and so it probably never ate nearly as much of the available woodland foods. Grey squirrels have only been here for a hundred years or so, yet they are now much more abundant than reds and eat a lot of hazels. They don't compete directly face to face because squirrels are active in daylight and dormice work the night shift. Dormice do have an advantage in that they are smaller and can more easily reach the tips of small branches to eat the nuts. Nevertheless, grey squirrels probably eat more hazel nuts than any other animals (including mice and various birds), and every nut they eat is one less that might feed a dormouse. In the Great Nut Hunt, most of the nuts found had been attacked by this species and nearly 70% of those that people thought had been eaten by dormice had also been eaten by squirrels.

Deer pose a more insidious problem for the future. Roe, red, fallow and muntjac are all increasing in numbers and distribution, all of them browse young shrubs. In some places the deer and rabbits prevent hazel regeneration completely. Hazels that are coppiced simply do not manage to regrow and after a few years the stool dies from lack of foliage development. In this way, areas of hazel, coppiced to help dormice, may end up as patches of bare ground and no use to dormice at all. This is a special problem in Britain because we have four introduced deer species as well as the native red and roe deer. Nowhere else within its entire European range does the dormouse have to coexist with so many species of deer. Red deer tend not to occur in dormouse habitats, but fallow deer are a particular problem because they live in herds which have more impact on the woodland than scattered individual roe deer. If deer nibbling stops hazels from regrowing after being coppiced, then there will be no nuts for anyone, dormice included.

A solution?

One way of dealing with this problem is for woodland managers to fence out the deer while newly coppiced hazel regrows. This can be done with piles of dead branches. By the time these have slowly broken down, the young hazel should be tall enough to be out of reach of the deer. A similar effect can be gained by pollarding the hazels. This enables the shrubs to rejuvenate, with all the benefits that brings, but regrowth now takes place about 1.5 metres above the ground where rabbits and most deer can't get at it. Another benefit is that hazels coppiced at ground level

do not produce nuts for about seven years, whereas pollarded hazels are back in production in only four or five years. This makes them available and useful for dormice quicker than in traditional coppice management systems. Of course, pollarding does mean that the harvested hazel poles are shorter and less useful than if they had been cut at ground level, but these days the poles are of negligible value anyway and coppicing is more about wildlife conservation rather than economic exploitation of the woods.

Dormice live among the smallest twigs and branches.

Habitat loss

The best dormouse habitat is in semi-natural woodland which has been in existence for at least 200 years, during which time a very mixed and species-rich plant community has developed. Past management has often enhanced the habitat by thinning out the canopy trees and rejuvenating the understorey by coppicing. However, nowadays only 23% of all woodland in England is of this type (and only 13% in Wales), the rest being plantations and various other woodland types that usually offer less good habitat for dormice. Much of what remains has also become less suitable for dormice due to lack of management, especially coppicing. Mature and unmanaged woods often become dark and shaded. This type of woodland, dominated by tall trees and with little understorey, is called 'high forest' and is more suited to the edible dormouse. Hazel dormice are scarce in such situations and generally live in the clearings and shrubby edges of the wood.

More than 32,000 hectares (79,000 acres) of ancient semi-natural woodland have been lost from England and Wales since 1930, so that this habitat now occupies only 2-3% of the land in these countries. Some areas have fared particularly badly, like south Yorkshire (one of the counties where dormice have been extinct since the late 19th century). Many of these potentially good dormouse woodlands have been replaced by farmland (representing 80% of the woodland lost), urban development (13%), roads and other forms of unsuitable habitat. Several surveys over the years have shown that old straggly hedges are important habitat for dormice, but hedgerows too have been severely depleted, with over 150,000 km lost since 1945. Hedgerows are also important as dispersal routes, allowing recolonisation of what is left of our ancient woodlands and copses and enabling movement between dormouse populations that might otherwise be isolated by farmland or other open ground.

Clearly wholesale removal of woodland would wipe out dormice locally, but even where secondary woodland has later grown on cleared ground, the habitat may take years to develop the diversity of woody plants that dormice need to support their lifestyle. This seems to be why many apparently suitable woodlands in central England do not have dormice. They were cleared long ago and replanted, but, by the time they had developed into good habitat, dormice had become extinct locally and were unable to spread back over the large areas of surrounding open land.

Deforestation left Britain one of the least wooded countries in Europe, but, paradoxically, there is now a greater area of woodland than for 200 years, due to planting, mostly of conifers. However, an extensive survey of woodlands in Herefordshire found dormice in only 23% of the recent (post AD 1600) woodlands sampled, compared to 46% of ancient semi-natural woodlands of similar size, reflecting the time it takes to establish diverse woodlands and for dormice to colonise them. Replacement of ancient woodland by plantations means that there are still large areas of trees and green patches on the map, but the habitat itself is a poor substitute for what has been lost.

Pigs

In the past it was traditional for local people to allow their pigs to wander about the woods in the autumn, fattening up on fallen beechmast and acorns. If they found the odd dormouse in its hibernation nest among the dead leaves, they would eat it. Even if the nest remained unnoticed, it was likely to get crushed under piggy feet. It is quite likely that some otherwise suitable woods are lacking dormice today because someone had their pigs roaming there 200 years ago. Once the dormice are gone from an isolated wood, they will not easily get back.

Coppicing and dormice

Removal of woodland is obviously bad, but a major cause of dormouse decline results from a subtle form of habitat loss due to the fact that woods are no longer managed the way they were. Coppice management in particular was widespread from well before the Middle Ages until the early 20th century. Coppicing happens to maintain almost ideal conditions for dormice by promoting vigorous growth of hazel, often below spaced out trees. The hazel would be cut every few years to yield a crop of poles. By the 19th century, coppice rotations (the time between major cutting) had lengthened to 14 or 15 years, ideal for heavily fruiting hazel and for dormice. Then in the 20th century, as coppice products ceased to be economically worthwhile, and as other fuels reduced demand for firewood and charcoal, managed woodlands were largely abandoned. Between 1900 and 1970 there was at least a 90% reduction in the area of actively coppiced woodland in Britain. Coppicing died out first in the north, and progressively southwards. So did the dormouse.

Once active management has ceased, old coppice becomes self-shaded and much of it forms standing dead wood. Dormice live at lower densities in derelict coppice and then die out as woodland development proceeds towards a form of high forest. Ultimately shading results in destruction of the understorey, removing the main food shrubs needed by dormice.

Modern coppicing is largely confined to south-east England, where much of it is of sweet chestnut, not hazel. Although this does support dormice, there are often few other trees present, unlike the medieval coppice-with-standards system that included oaks, ash and other species of taller trees. Modern coppicing also requires short rotations, usually less than seven years, continually removing hazel before it fruits profusely and thus not recreating a good dormouse habitat. Ironically, reinstatement of coppicing for wildlife conservation is also often not beneficial to dormice. This is because it frequently features short rotations which are demonstrably effective for certain woodland flowers and butterflies, but remove the hazel before it fruits. Conservation coppicing also often entails cutting too large a proportion of tiny woodland nature reserves. This has the effect of making a substantial part of the wood unsuitable for dormice whilst the coppice regrows to maturity, meanwhile leaving insufficient suitable habitat to sustain a viable dormouse population.

Thinning of tall trees, another form of management, encourages a sprawling and productive shrub layer. Lack of it leaves regenerating saplings and shrubs to compete vigorously, generating a habitat in which most of the trees are of similar age (without fruit or flowers for their early years). Young trees, drawn up in unmanaged woodland, tend to be spindly and unstable even in a light breeze. They also tend to have few horizontal boughs linking them. This growth form is likely to make it more difficult for dormice to move about or feed in the canopy.

Once the economic incentive to manage small woodlands has gone, there is little interest in (nor the money to do so) fencing out free ranging sheep and cattle, who then trample and browse the shrubs and saplings. Ultimately a form of parkland results, with widely spaced large trees, little or no regeneration and no shrubs, completely unsuitable

Hazel nuts, eaten high up in the tree canopy, are the single most important food for Muscardinus.

for dormice. This is now the situation in many of the Welsh woodlands. A survey revealed that over 60% of known dormouse sites in Wales were threatened by clearance, farm animals, or other inappropriate management.

Habitat fragmentation

As more woodland is destroyed, the remaining fragments become progressively further separated. This is clearly illustrated by the historical reduction of woodland in Warwickshire, where about 80% of the county was under continuous woodland in prehistoric times. By the time of the Domesday survey (1086) the forest was broken up into more than 20 fragments and by late Victorian times it covered only 2.9% of the county, in more than 50 fragments. In 1970, Warwickshire's woodland (including regenerated and replanted woodland) was down to 2.6% of the county, scattered among about 60 fragments, some of them over 10 kilometres from their nearest neighbour. Small dormouse populations would be likely to die out in small areas of woodland, and lack of recolonisation over wide areas of open ground would mean that the extinctions were permanent. It is small wonder that, until we staged a reintroduction, there was only a single known locality for the dormouse in late 20th century Warwickshire.

A survey in Herefordshire provided more details of these issues. Dormice were less often present in recently planted woods than in ancient woodland and less often found in woods with few hedges or other dispersal routes in the vicinity. Only a third of the isolated woods of less than 20 hectares (49 acres) had dormice present, contrasting with more than three-quarters of the woods larger then 20 hectares. So this might be the minimum area of suitable habitat that will support a viable population in the long term. This could be because larger woods are more likely to contain the array of plant species and habitat structures needed to support dormice. More likely, it reflects the vulnerability of small population sizes in smaller woods. There just aren't enough animals to cope with disasters like fires, several bad breeding years in succession or removal of part of the wood's shrubs through coppicing or clearance.

The snag is that nearly half of the remaining ancient woodland in England and Wales now occurs in areas of less than 20 hectares. Only 17% of all ancient woodland sites are bigger than this, big enough to support dormice in the long term. The vulnerability of dormouse populations in these fragments is made worse by the isolation that results from intensive use of their surroundings for farming or urban purposes. The problem with identifying 20 hectares as the minimum area needed to support a viable dormouse population is that dormice are often found in woods that are much smaller than this. Indeed some of the best sites are copses where, because of their small size, the edge effect is greater and there is little shading of the shrubs. However, many of these sites are linked to others by hedgerows and woodland strips, reducing their isolation and increasing their effective size. The danger lies in sites which are small and isolated. Dormice may occur there now, but the probability of their long-term survival is low.

Fortunately, dormice also live in other woody habitats, particularly shrubby woodlands such as we see in Devon and Dorset. They also live in hedges and even scrub encroaching on heathland or downland. However, these sites are often in a state of change and many do not have a very secure future.

Concern is frequently expressed when new road developments threaten to destroy a small wood containing dormice, but this distracts from a much wider issue. Small sites will probably lose their dormice anyway, but the road itself creates a potential barrier between the remaining woodland fragments. Roads frequently sever many of the linking features that would help dormice to move between one small area and another, increasing the vulnerability of small populations.

Widening the A21

The A21 links London and Hastings in Kent and dormice live alongside it. Parts of it were sufficiently narrow that trees met overhead and dormice might have crossed via the branches, or run 20 metres from one roadside hedge to the other. Piecemeal widening of this road has created a dual carriageway, often with wide grassy verges, crossing 100 kilometres of the best dormouse habitats in Britain. As the road is widened the immediate damage may be to
obliterate a few dormice as many small woods and the roadside hedges are destroyed. However, the long-term effect is a substantial obstacle to animal movements. Isolating woodland fragments in this way leaves non-viable, inbred populations that must eventually die out. This is a danger, not just to dormice, but also to many other species. The barrier effect is more significant, although less obvious, than the threat posed by just destroying a few bits of habitat.

How did the dormouse cross the road?

The problem of modern roads restricting the natural movements and dispersal of wildlife has been recognised as a serious threat for many years, although not in Britain it seems. To lessen the dangers of collisions with traffic, as well as the long term threat to dispersal, special 'habitat bridges' have been built in many countries. These consist of a normal bridge, but carrying strips of grassland or woodland instead of another road. They appear to work, and have been built in France, Belgium, the Netherlands, Germany, Austria and probably other places too, but Britain lags behind. Yet Britain has the greatest problems with habitat fragmentation because those other countries usually have large areas of habitat remaining intact as they have more space. We don't.

As part of the planning for widening the A21 London-Hastings road, we were asked to carry out dormouse surveys. These showed that the proposed widening and bypass around Lamberhurst would affect dormice badly. So, as part of the negotiations with the National Trust over release of land needed for the bypass, I suggested that a habitat bridge should be built linking Lamberhurst with the National Trust property at Scotney Castle. This was built in 2006. As it happens, this is not the best place for dormice, but better than nothing and it has been good for other wildlife. A visit in 2009 confirmed that at least seven species (including a mole!) were using the bridge to cross the dual carriageway by-pass, although the shrubs had not yet developed sufficiently for dormice. The bridge is also good for people, allowing them to walk or cycle without danger from traffic, direct from the village to the castle woods and gardens. It looks nice, too, in a very attractive part of the country. Yet despite these advantages, there were strenuous objections from the Highways Agency who grumbled that, if a habitat bridge was built (at great expense), the nature conservationists would be unable to agree on what sort of habitat it should carry. Yet whatever habitat was established on the bridge, it would be better than a four-lane dual carriageway! So, the dormice may have enabled Britain to get its first habitat bridge across a new road, a decade or more after many other European countries had recognised their value.

Meanwhile in Japan a similar situation had arisen. A new road sliced through valuable habitat for the Japanese dormouse and to reduce the barrier effect of the road it was agreed that a special bridge would be constructed. This one consists of a steel gantry, also used to support some sign boards. The bridge is about 20 metres long and the upper part forms a tunnel about 1.5 metres wide, enclosed by a steel mesh to protect the dormice from predatory birds. The tunnel was filled with brushwood and ropes to provide cover for small mammals. Japanese wood mice discovered the bridge within a few weeks and in less than a year dormice were using the bridge too, even nesting there and producing young. This bridge was expensive, costing about £100,000, because it was made specially.

However, arboreal animals like dormice are small and could use a smaller and cheaper bridge. A simple 'arboreal animal pathway', suspended across a rural road in Japan, was used by four mammal species within weeks. In Britain we have had some experimental dormouse bridges built, using suspended tunnels made of wire mesh. Unfortunately nobody has monitored them properly so we do not know if the dormice use them. Some were built in the wrong place and serious negative publicity has resulted, claiming they are a waste of money. Moreover, it is argued that they are not necessary as dormice will cross roads and may even nest on the central reservation! This is true, some dormice might cross a road occasionally, but how often and how many others will find the road a daunting obstruction? This we do not know. The Japanese experiment showed that, even though the road was less than 20 metres wide and had little traffic, animals sought out the arboreal pathway and used it 800 times in three months, showing just how much they valued it in preference to coming to the ground and dashing across the road. In Britain ropes have been suggested but I have never seen any evidence that dormice will actually use them.

We need more research on the issue. Moreover, adapting ready-made structures (like traffic signboard gantries) to help wildlife cross roads will be considerably cheaper than building specific bridges. Anyway, the cost is small compared to the expense of building a major road. It would be a small price to pay for ameliorating the long-term threats that roads pose to dormice and other small animals.

Conservation of the hazel dormouse

Other parts of this book have surveyed the depressingly long list of things that are bad for dormice, accounting for their present-day scarcity. In fact, dormouse ecology is like a long chain of weak links. If any of them gives way – habitat quality, weather, population size, dispersal corridors – then extinction follows. This implies that we should try to stop or at least lessen those many threats that the dormouse faces in Britain. Unfortunately we cannot do very much about the climate, which makes it all the more important that habitat management and environmental protection are the best we can manage.

Our national dormouse conservation policy, developed as part of English Nature's Species Recovery Programme, has three main strands. First we should defend dormice where they still occur, through good habitat management. This includes provision of nest boxes, which not only benefit dormice, but also provide a means of obtaining regular information about dormouse numbers. This is the basis for the National Dormouse Monitoring Programme, in which teams of volunteers monitor more than 6,000 nest boxes at 220 sites nationwide. This provides information each year about relative numbers (number of adults per 50 nest boxes), litter sizes and body weight. It has been going for a decade now and was the first national monitoring programme for any terrestrial British mammal, providing a lead for others to follow. Annual data analyses enable comparisons to be made between years and also between different parts of the country.

The management of habitats for dormice essentially involves avoiding the negative factors described earlier in this book. Woodland trees should not grow so densely that they cast a deep shade, they should be thinned out. Hazels should be coppiced to rejuvenate them, but only at long intervals, allowing plenty of time for the shrubs to produce nuts year after year. Management should be in small patches so as not to clear large areas all at once or create large areas of uniform habitat. Patchiness and diversity are what is needed. Nest boxes should be supplied whenever possible and farm animals should be kept out of dormouse woods by using suitable fencing. None of this need cost huge amounts of money and in any case there are various types of conservation and woodland management grants available to help.

The second part of the hazel dormouse conservation strategy aims to reintroduce dormice to areas from which they have been lost. Since 1993 several hundred were released at carefully selected sites within the former range of dormice in England (see *Putting dormice back on the map,* page 86). It may seem trivial to set up a dozen new populations, when the losses have been so great and so widespread. It might also be viewed as a kind of 'wildlife gardening' – planting dormice in strategic places. But there have been huge benefits in terms of mobilising support, which would not have been given to less popular animals. Even journalists now take dormice seriously!

Indeed one of the main lessons of the whole dormouse project has been to show that concentration on a single species (provided it is the right one) can be highly effective. People have often asked, 'Why focus on just the dormouse? Surely it is better to conserve habitats and let the species look after themselves.' This is certainly a good approach, but not the only one that is valid. In fact the dormouse is an excellent example of what we call a 'flagship species'. If the flagship is present in a naval fleet, so are all the other support vessels, and the whole fleet functions efficiently as a single system. The same applies to dormice. Look after the dormice and the flowers, butterflies, small mammals and birds, the rest of the 'woodland fleet' will all be there too. Manage the woods suitably for dormice and many other species will benefit as well. At the same time a woodland is created which everyone would agree is a nice place to visit and good for wildlife. Practical conservation management is in the hands of county wildlife trusts and other woodland owners. Many of them offer opportunities for members and the public to see dormice. The People's Trust for Endangered Species and the Mammal Society offer dormouse training courses and conferences to learn more about them. A special dormouse conference in 2002 was attended by over 120 people!

A third part of the dormouse conservation strategy has been to raise the public profile of this animal. We have tried to put across the message that dormice are different and that conserving them is not just a sentimental whimsy. Protecting dormice has many benefits, including safeguarding woodlands and hedgerows from destruction and encouraging plant and insect diversity in our forests. We have all come a long way. Now we know more about the dormouse than about many other species that are more common. The dormouse has become part of the national wildlife monitoring programme. Its conservation involves large numbers of volunteers and it is no longer the creature of mystery that even professional biologists never saw. Instead dormouse photographs frequently appear in daily newspapers and magazines and it has become a familiar icon of British natural history like the hedgehog and the otter.

Will global warming come to the rescue?

Probably not. This is because mere warmth is not enough. Warmer weather may bring more cloudiness and this will do little to increase the quantities of flowers and fruits available as food. Even if global warming is good for dormice, this will still not help very much. Their habitat is now so fragmented in many counties that increased numbers will not help them spread to areas where they have died out, especially in open country. Even if global warming made the north of England more suitable for dormice once again, they are unlikely to benefit very much unless a lot of tree and hedgerow planting is done to help recolonise isolated dormouse-free woods.

Putting dormice back on the map

The dormouse seems to have disappeared from at least six counties and now occurs almost entirely south of a line between Suffolk and Shropshire. Part of our long-term conservation strategy involves reintroducing them to some of the areas where they have become locally extinct.

Taking dormice from one place to release them somewhere else is likely to result in losses, making the species rarer still. Only a few wild animals were ever likely to be available (rescued from cats for example), too few to form the basis for released populations. So it was important to see if we could use animals raised in captivity, especially those rescued from impending winter when they were too small to survive. Dormice often produce litters in the autumn, born too late to survive the winter. The young must weigh at least 12-15 g to be sure of having sufficient fat to last until the following spring. So, juveniles found in October or later weighing less than this can be taken into captivity without affecting the wild population of the following year. These can be fed well so they survive the winter and breed next season, producing plenty of animals for release. With the help of volunteers in the Dormouse Captive Breeders Group, stocks of captive dormice have been built up in this way without reducing wild populations. However, these animals are often tame and rather overweight. How might they cope in the wild? This problem underlies all reintroductions based on captive-bred animals, yet surprisingly few attempts have been made to compare the success of wild-caught and captive-bred mammals after their release in unfamiliar surroundings.

We found that captive-bred animals remained close to their point of release, travelling significantly less far than wild-caught dormice. They were also more dependent on artificially supplied food, implying slower adaptation to life in the wild. Although more of them were probably lost to accidents (including owls) soon after release than the more experienced wild-caught individuals, captive-bred dormice nevertheless managed surprisingly well. They were often fatter than wild dormice, allowing them to breed earlier in the summer. We concluded that reintroductions based on using captive-bred dormice were feasible. Losses resulting from their unwariness (for example) could be compensated for by releasing larger numbers that could fairly easily be supplied from captive stock.

Small numbers of animals face a disproportionately high risk of extinction from chance events and a release group of less than 20 animals has a high probability of not building up its numbers soon enough to ensure long-term survival. So the more dormice that are

Captive breeding

Country people used to find dormice in the winter when they were coppicing or working on hedges, and take them home for the children to keep. However, dormice need a lot of attention and do not normally come out during the day. So, keeping them as pets is not a good idea and taking them for this purpose is illegal. Nevertheless, a group of zoos and experienced keepers now operate a captive breeding programme, based on rescued animals. The purpose is to supply batches of animals for reintroduction projects. Captive dormice are kept in spacious cages with plenty of branches among which to climb. The animals must be fed on fresh fruit (apple is very popular), grapes, sunflower seeds, biscuits and a variety of other materials. Normal rodent pellets are an inadequate diet for these specialised animals. Each dormouse has its own nest box, although they often choose to share. Males have to be kept separate during the breeding season. A small plastic tray of earth and moss is provided from late summer, within which the animals hibernate when the weather gets cold. They need to have suitable nesting materials provided and should not be kept too warm over winter. The moss has to be dampened by sprinkling water over it once a week. Food can be withdrawn or provided infrequently during the winter, but water must always be available. The animals will emerge in the spring and need feeding continuously from then onwards. Females may give birth any time after about mid-May, and need their own private nest box (and preferably their own family cage) in which to raise the young. Healthy females may manage to produce a second litter about August or September. Keeping edible dormice in captivity is probably illegal and releasing them certainly is. They are bad-tempered animals, active mainly at night and do not make good pets.

IUCN guidelines

It is irresponsible to release dormice without careful preparation and making provision for monitoring their success. There is no point in releasing dormice if they die out again, for the same reasons as before. To avoid this sort of waste, the International Union for the Conservation of Nature offers guidelines to encourage proper attention to planning and to protect the welfare of released animals. Reintroductions should only be carried out where:

1. There is good historical evidence of previous occurrence at or near the site.
2. Natural recolonisation is un-likely. For the dormouse, this includes areas now geographically isolated from reservoir populations and sites from which dormice have been lost due to lack of appropriate habitat or management.
3. Factors causing local extinction have been identified and rectified.
4. Available habitat is sufficient to support a viable population. With dormice this means at least 20 hectares (49 acres) in isolated sites, 50 hectares (123 acres) where the habitat is less than ideal.
5. The animals used are genetically similar to the natural population. We have only one species of Muscardinus, with no local subspecies, so this is not a major problem.
6. Obtaining animals for release does not jeopardise existing wild populations.

Animals should have a veterinary check before release. This was not feasible at the time of our early releases, but is now a regular part of the procedure.

---

released at once the better, but large numbers are difficult to manage in the field. A group of more than 50 takes too long for volunteer assistants to complete the feeding rounds, especially if the release cages are well spaced out. We therefore aimed to release animals in batches of about 30.

Dormouse ecology is complex and simply letting them go is likely to leave many of them unable to cope with the difficulties of living in an unfamiliar place and in danger of early starvation. Dormice require a sequence of suitable foods to be available in the tree and shrub canopy throughout the summer, but in an unfamiliar place, how will they know where to find the next source of food as each type ceases to be available? What can be done to help them adjust to the wild? When is the best time of year for release? Reintroduction of this species

Good dormouse habitat has plenty of branches linking trees and shrubs, with sunny glades where shrubs can produce fruit and flowers.

is complicated, which is why we did so much extra research before beginning a full-scale programme of releases.

Simply letting animals go ('hard release') may be satisfactory for generalist feeders, but a specialist like the dormouse may not adjust to its new surroundings fast enough to avoid starvation. Radio tracking revealed that hard-released animals lost weight, travelled further, and frequently scattered. Some were never encountered again. Clearly hard release is not the way to do it. So we devised a 'soft release' procedure, in which the animals received support before and after release and also had time to adjust to their new surroundings before having to fend for themselves. For at least a week, dormice were put – in their nest boxes – in large pre-release cages fixed to shrubs before being allowed free. Here they became accustomed to the sights, sounds and smells of their new surroundings. After release, fresh food was continually replaced in the cages, providing a supplement if the dormice were unable to find sufficient natural food. Up to 200 other nest boxes were put up in the surrounding habitat.

The best time of year to release dormice would seem to be late summer when their favourite foods are most abundant. However, the small number of animals would then be reduced by winter mortality before they had a chance to breed. If they were released in early summer, they would have time to breed and they and their progeny would have time to fatten up before winter. However, early summer is the time when foods for dormice are in short supply: flowers are over, but fruits are not yet ripe. Our studies confirmed that dormice released in the autumn fed well. Those released in early summer quickly lost weight, which could be regained if artificial food was provided. Additional food (in the form of fruit, seeds and biscuits) had the further advantage that it acted like a magnet and kept the animals from scattering. Being together meant they were more likely to breed early on and therefore had longer in which to raise their young before winter overtook them. This is why dormouse reintroductions have all taken place in early summer (usually June), using pre-release cages and post-release feeding until ripe hazel nuts became available in August. But the animals often seemed to prefer rich tea biscuits to new hazel nuts, so once the natural food was abundant, our supply of artificial provisions was cut off to encourage proper foraging behaviour.

Male dormice can be highly aggressive in the breeding season so the release cages were spaced 100 metre apart, approximately the diameter of a dormouse home range. Each cage contained one male plus one or two females, with separate nest boxes for each animal. At least 200 nest boxes were set out in the wood before the release. These provided vital shelter, especially in bad weather, and a means of monitoring the continued presence and breeding success of the new population. However, this number of boxes is expensive and the need for volunteers to check the cages daily for six weeks in summer means that organising a release is a complicated and costly business. But it is unfair on the animals to cut corners, releasing them without support or late in the season.

A viable population of dormice needs at least 20 hectares (about 50 acres) of suitable habitat. Releasing them into smaller areas may well succeed, but only in the short term. The tree and shrub layer should be varied and include hazel and other useful species. Finding suitable sites for releasing dormice proved to be quite difficult, especially in the counties where they had become extinct. In fact the habitats available

Release guidelines

A scientifically based procedure for releasing dormice:

1. Ensure at least 200 nest boxes are deployed to provide shelter for the animals and a means of monitoring their future presence and breeding success.

2. Use captive-bred animals, plus any available wild-caught dormice(those rescued from cats, etc.)

3. Plan for releases in early summer (e.g. June).

4. Keep and release animals in pairs (or 1 male + 2 females).

5. Use pre-release cages, 100 metres apart, to acclimatise the animals on site for ten days. The animals' own nest boxes from captivity are used to take them to the release cages, then they and their boxes are installed inside.

6. Open the cages during fine weather, leaving insufficient space for squirrels to enter.

7. Continue regular supply of fresh fruit, biscuits, nuts and sunflower seeds until hazels are ripe on nearby shrubs, then discontinue feeding.

8. Monitor nest boxes monthly during subsequent summers.

were often so poor that it was easy to see why dormice had died out in so many areas. It was soon apparent that few suitable woods remain in most of northern England. In Yorkshire, for example, many woods have become dominated by sycamore at the expense of vital shrubs. In Staffordshire and Derbyshire sheep nibbling is widespread, again destroying the shrub layer. Poor soils also inhibit hazel growth and many woods around urban areas are too disturbed by people and lack food-producing shrubs. It is easy to see why reintroduction in such areas would be futile and a waste of dormice.

The first reintroduction was to Cambridgeshire where the dormouse seems not to have been seen since 1904. A suitably large (140 hectare/346 acres) wood was found and in July 1993 we released 19 dormice there – some wild-caught and some captive-bred. The weather was dreadful and the captive-bred animals had probably never experienced rain before. Nevertheless, radio tracking confirmed that the dormice soon learned their way about, visiting neighbouring release cages and using nearby nest boxes. Some of the dormice undertook lengthy excursions, then returned to their cages by taking short cuts, passing through areas they had not previously visited. In fact they found their way about rather better than we did, as the wood was so big it was easy to get lost in, especially after dark!

At least 36 young were born in the first summer, probably the first baby dormice in Cambridgeshire for nearly 100 years. Two females even produced second litters that summer, their first families having died probably due to the awful weather. For the first few years, numbers built up slowly and we feared that the dormice had failed to establish themselves. However, it seems that they often did not use the nest boxes, so they were present in much larger numbers than we thought. Nevertheless, we did lose quite a few to an enterprising weasel who found out what nest boxes contained and made a meal of several dormice. Fortunately it died or went to live somewhere else before too much damage was done. By 1999 the Cambridge dormice had spread throughout their wood. That year, over 50 animals were found in the nest boxes, a substantial increase on the number released. The total population must have been much larger because only a small part of the wood is actually monitored. In Autumn 2000 similar numbers were present and there were high hopes of spread to other nearby copses via the linking hedges, but the dormice are unlikely to get very far as Cambridgeshire is a pretty open sort of county.

We next tried Nottinghamshire, another county where dormice had become extinct since the 1880s. This time, unlike Cambridge, we could only find a relatively poor area of habitat in which to release dormice. Nevertheless, survival over the first summer was similar to the earlier project and some more animals were released in 1995. Despite an encouraging start, the Nottinghamshire population seemed to fizzle out. Only occasional animals were found in 1996 and 1997 and by 1999 there was little evidence of any dormouse activity. A single animal was seen in 2001, and a dead one was found in a tawny owl nest box in 2002. The future of this population remains uncertain. There were other problems too. Several of the captive-bred animals were really too fat and some were badly affected by mites. Perhaps we should not have released them, but there were no facilities available for keeping them longer in captivity.

By 2010 there had been a succession of releases in various other counties, one or two per year, 17 in all. In 1996, Cheshire received its first dormice in nearly 100 years and they have done well, spreading through the small wooded areas available, with evidence of breeding and population growth within four years. Some managed to cross a river on overhanging trees and became Welsh dormice for a while. Dormice were known from only one site in Warwickshire until a release took place in 1998. Half these animals were captive-bred, the rest had been rescued from the path of the Channel Tunnel Rail Link in Kent. The dormice bred in the weeks following release, despite a period of horrible weather, and by late 2001 some of the original group were still alive and the population seemed to have grown. Subsequent changes to the woodland have probably meant that this colony has died out.

Dormice still occur in Buckinghamshire, but at widely scattered localities. The release of 41 animals in 1998 near Milton Keynes included both captive-bred and wild animals 'rescued' from Kent. Yet again the project ran into bad weather, but in the following years numbers appeared to increase, although few were found in 2003; perhaps the dormice were not using nest boxes very much and so could not be detected reliably. Since then, numbers have built up and spread through the wood, aided by nest boxes and supported by a very enthusiastic team of local volunteers.

More than a score of dormouse sites were known in Yorkshire 150 years ago, and the species was reported there as recently as the 1980s. However, despite extensive searches, no evidence of Yorkshire dormice was found in the 1990s. So, some animals were released at a private site in 1999, within the main area of 19th century records. Coppicing had been reinstated in these woodlands, and hedges connected the release area to extensive potential dormouse habitat. The animals bred in the year of release and again in 2000. They should be able to survive, but there have been few signs of them lately. Subsequently, dormice were released in Suffolk, Bedfordshire and Derbyshire, but it is probably too soon to say how well they are doing.

Has it been a success?

If these new dormouse populations were still thriving in a hundred years' time we could claim success, but we need to gauge 'success' long before then because people won't wait that long to find out!

Success comes in stages:

Stage 1. Release accomplished by July, with animals returning to feed in their cages, even if they do not live in them all the time.

Stage 2. Young born at the new site, preferably by September of the first year.

Stage 3. Some animals survive the first winter, being present in nest boxes in year 2.

Stage 4. Birth of second generation young (i.e. born to females who themselves were born at the site). This is difficult to demonstrate unless the original release cohort are permanently marked.

Stage 5. More adults present than were originally released (i.e. survival by now exceeds losses).

Stage 6. Evidence of dispersal found.

By 2008 two sites (Cambridgeshire and Cheshire) had reached stage 7 and there is no reason why they should not now be regarded as secure populations. Eight more sites had reached at least stage 6. The more recent populations have reached at least stage 3, often stage 4 or 5. Stage 4 was reached in Nottinghamshire, although this population seems not to have thrived. Two others appear to have fizzled out, making a probable failure rate of three out of 16 sites. The rest represent an 80% success rate for these reintroductions.

There are other measures of success too, because reintroductions of charismatic species like the dormouse offer potential benefits in terms of publicity and fund raising. They also raise awareness of environmental issues and the need for active conservation management. This is exemplified by the release in Cheshire, where the local Wildlife Trust enjoyed the highest media coverage of any of its activities ever, ranging from an article in *The Times* to visits from TV personalities. Favourable publicity attracts all kinds of support, and that project gained local sponsorship and grant aid in spite of the exact site being kept secret. A longer-term benefit was to highlight the wildlife richness of the whole reintroduction area and encourage production of an overall management plan, involving private landowners and many different interest groups. Creating suitable conditions for reintroducing and maintaining a viable population of dormice has also served to support a wide range of other wildlife, in what is a very beautiful area of Cheshire that had been previously largely overlooked.

Marking dormice

Marking dormice gives each an individual identity and enables more detailed study of their lives, but it does require a licence. Dormice can be marked temporarily by fur clipping. Small patches clipped out on shoulders and haunches (like marking hedgehogs) allows combinations to be used to identify individuals until the next moult. The mark will then be obscured by fresh fur growth. Permanent marking was done by tattooing a small number in each ear. These are often difficult to read and this is not a technique we have found amateurs could use very easily. Nowadays Passive Implanted Transponders (PIT tags) are injected under the skin to mark a wide variety of pets and laboratory animals. They are like tiny pieces of pencil lead that can be read like a supermarket bar-code reader.

These became available about the time we started the reintroduction programme, but were really too large to be put into a hazel dormouse. Smaller PIT tags are now available and all released animals are now tagged to maintain a record of their identity and survival. PIT tags are expensive (£5 each), not easy to apply without risk to the animal and the readers also cost a lot (£150+). Again this is not really suitable for amateur use. On the Continent, one study involved permanent marking of dormice by cutting off their toes in various combinations. This would be illegal in Britain. One of my research assistants did carry out this procedure, in direct defiance of my instructions, saying that it was the only certain way of marking the animals for life. I sacked him.

Future reintroductions

Reintroductions are popular, but have serious drawbacks. They encourage people to believe (wrongly!) that local extinction does not matter, because animals can always be reintroduced. They also allow developers to propose removal of populations to allow lucrative urban developments, with the animals being let go somewhere else. But reintroduction should always be seen as a policy of last resort. Conservation of dormice (and other species) is best done by defending them where they occur, not by shifting them to where they have already died out. However, translocating animals like the dormouse can help put them back on the map where natural recolonisation is unlikely. If captive-bred animals can be used, then wild populations will not be compromised.

It is also important to discourage frivolous 'reintroductions'. We are frequently asked to supply 'a few' dormice for release into gardens and other unsuitable places, to indulge the whims of well meaning people. Others ask for dormice to breed them for release. We have refused such requests because release projects must be properly managed, with the animals' best interests put first. The management of future reintroductions is now undertaken by the People's Trust for Endangered Species, in collaboration with the Common Dormouse Captive Breeders Group.

THE EDIBLE DORMOUSE
What's in a name?

As an introduced species, brought here only in 1902, the edible dormouse had no common English name. In the early days it was sometimes called 'Chinchilla', a reference to its superficial similarity to the fluffy grey South American rodent that is occasionally kept as a pet. For some reason it was also called 'Spanish rat'. Later the name 'sleeper' was used, a translation of its German name which refers to its long hibernation period. Yet another name is the 'fat' dormouse, a reference to the fact that it feeds extensively before hibernation and stores up a lot of fat to last the winter. Some adults may then weigh more than 250 g and appear distinctly podgy.

The name 'edible' dormouse arises because, in many countries of southern Europe, this animal has been a frequent item on the menu. In Roman times it was specially raised for the table, although there is little evidence that this was ever done in Britain and our present-day population was not established here by the Romans.

To avoid the confusion caused by having a whole host of common names, scientists use a system in which each animal is given a unique name, in Latin. Latin names are internationally recognised and provide stability from one century to the next. Unfortunately, there is confusion here too. Carl von Linné, who devised the modern scientific system of naming things, lived in Sweden. He had never seen one of these animals himself because they do not occur that far north. His official description of the animal was based on information sent to him by letter from Slovenia. He named the creature *Sciurus glis* in 1766, thinking it was some kind of squirrel, an obvious error.

Meanwhile, the animal had been called *Glis* by the Romans, and this was adopted in 1762 as its official scientific name. However, the technicalities of modern scientific naming are such that the use of the name *Glis glis* may actually be incorrect. As a result, there was a recent proposal to abolish this name and substitute another that had been proposed for it long ago, namely *Myoxus glis*. If that name were adopted, it would cause still more complications over the naming of other animals; meanwhile a great many ordinary people routinely use 'Glis' as the animal's everyday name because it is shorter and simpler than any of the others! Fortunately, there is a special panel of international experts who sort out such muddles once and for all. They have decided that we should use *Glis glis* as the animal's official internationally recognised scientific name, but we can call it what we like in our own language of course and some householders have some pretty pungent words to describe it, because this is not a cute creature like the hazel dormouse, but something completely different.

Roman 'Gliraria'

The Romans kept these animals in large earthenware pots (called 'dolia'), where they could be fattened up for the table. The pots would be stored in special dormouse gardens; both the pots and the gardens have been referred to as 'Gliraria'. One such pot was found in the excavation of Verulamium (St Albans), but otherwise there is no evidence that edible dormice were kept in Roman Britain. The pots had a series of shelves inside so that many dormice could sit there at once. They would first be fattened up, then cooled by pouring water over the clay pot. This would then evaporate, keeping the animals cool and encouraging them to hibernate. In this state they would require no more food, but (unlike dead animals) they would not decay. This way, large numbers of glis could be kept at no cost and simply taken out and cooked when needed. They were so fat that they were 'self basting' if roasted on a spit. Other methods of cooking included first soaking them in honey. Latin recipes still exist. I have never eaten one, but I imagine it tastes rather like squirrel, mild, a bit tough and with very little meat on the numerous bones – about enough for a sandwhich.

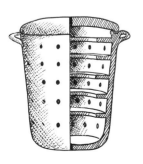 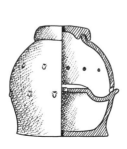 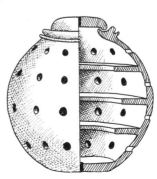

History of the edible dormouse in England

It is widely reported that Lord Walter Rothschild introduced the edible dormouse to Britain in 1902. He released a few at his home in Tring Park (Hertfordshire) about 100 kilometres north-west of London. We know little more than that. We don't know how many he let go nor from where the original animals came. A local naturalist, Major Stanley Flower, said they 'probably came from Germany or Switzerland', but he offered no evidence in support of his opinion. Anyway, this statement was not published until 1947, nearly half a century after the event. This is plenty of time in which to get confused, but his information has been repeated in several important books since then and seems to be widely accepted as fact. More recently, the grandson of the man who obtained the original animals has insisted that they came from Hungary. This story seems more reliable, not least because Major Flower himself did not see his first edible dormouse until 1929, over a quarter of a century after the introduction had taken place. Moreover, he said that they had been released on or about 4th February, an unlikely time to liberate an animal that hibernates. I have not been able to find confirmation of any of this in Rothschild's archived correspondence. Perhaps we will one day be able to sort this out by using DNA fingerprinting techniques. However, a recent attempt to do this simply showed that edible dormice were so similar all across Europe that it is not presently possible to tell where ours might have originated.

The edible dormouse is a prime example of the principle, 'Act in haste, repent at leisure'. This seems to be the lesson to be learnt from almost every introduction of an alien species to places it has not been able to reach naturally. Within a short time after their release at Tring, edible dormice were being blamed for damage to nearby crops and efforts were made to exterminate them. Many were killed, but by the mid 1920s they had become quite numerous around Tring Park and people started to complain about the damage and nuisance they caused in houses. Domestic intrusions were well documented from 1935 onwards and have become increasingly frequent as the years have gone by. Glis numbers appear to have risen steadily for at least the last ten years.

A growing household pest

The household problems caused by edible dormice include gnawing of electric wires, with shocking consequences to the animals, but also a serious risk of causing fires. The animals also raid food bowls and kitchen stores, gnaw bars of soap and generally make themselves a nuisance, running about at night. They drown in attic water tanks, so turning on a bath tap results in a furry sludge coming out. They drown in lavatory pans too. I was once shown a linen cupboard where the animals had nestled down among the immaculate whites, but they had evidently been feeding on purple elder berries the night before. I also met a man whose factory burglar alarms were being triggered so often at night the *neighbours complained and police refused to respond, yet if he switched them off his insurance policy was invalid. He was trying to sell the business with this dilemma unresolved. For him, these animals were more than just a nuisance. Between 1943 and 1961, nearly 600 edible dormice were trapped in houses in the Amersham area alone and today it is not unusual to hear of 50 or more being removed from a single house.*

'I'm sure I heard something, Dear.'

Distribution of edible dormice

The edible dormouse is found across Mediterranean Europe, from northern Spain to Turkey and beyond the Black Sea. In the north its limit is about 55° latitude, almost reaching the Baltic, but not the Netherlands or Denmark. Whilst it is said to be declining in parts of Europe, the edible dormouse does not appear threatened in Britain. Here its population is expanding and there is little prospect of its becoming extinct here. The British edible dormouse population is confined to the Chiltern hills, within about 35 kilometres of where it was first introduced at Tring, about 100 kilometres north-west of London. The main area extends west to the Bledlow Ridge, south to High Wycombe and east to Potters Bar.

Curiously, although numbers have steadily built up, this does not seem to have pushed the animals into dispersing very far. Since the first distribution survey in the 1950s, the animal's range has remained much the same. I sent out a questionnaire in 1995 to residents in the Chilterns and the replies confirmed that edible dormice had spread very little in the 90 years since they were first established in this country. However, this survey did suggest that there had been some increase in both numbers and distribution in recent years. Nearly 70% of the 1995 records came from Buckinghamshire; most of the others were from Hertfordshire, with one report from as far east as Stevenage (about 30 kilometres from Tring).

A record from near Windsor (Berkshire) indicates further spread into the woodlands well south of Tring. A few isolated reports suggest that edible dormice have also been carried long distances to various other English counties. In 1941, one was found in Shropshire, over 200 kilometres to the north-west and another was reported from Sandy in Bedfordshire, about 45 kilometres north-east of Tring. Presumably these distant records are of animals that were carried accidentally, perhaps on lorries loaded with stuff in which the animals had been nesting. However, edible dormice are being spread about increasingly often. People catch them in their houses and don't want to kill them. (How anyway?) So they let them go outdoors. Obviously this needs to be done well away from the house or the crafty beasts will soon return,

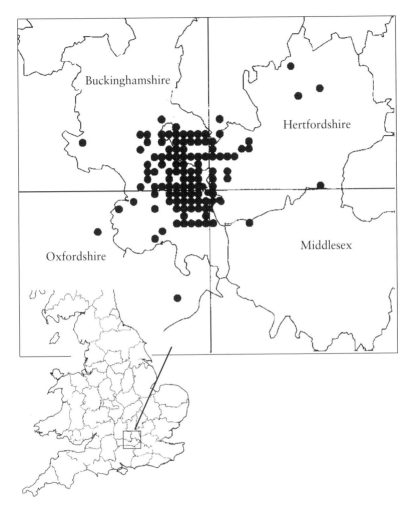

Distribution of the edible dormouse remains centred on the Chilterns, the area where it was first released over one hundred years ago. Recent reports of animals found far away (e.g. in Dorset and the New Forest) have not been included.

so they are taken somewhere else to be let go. This is actually illegal, so it is difficult to get people to own up and supply details. However, I do know of one certain case where edible dormice were taken to the New Forest in Hampshire (much of which is ideal Glis habitat) and another case where they were released in Wytham Woods near Oxford. This is the main study site for Oxford University biologists, but they seem not to have noticed their new inhabitants yet, so maybe they died out. More recently they have been found near Poole in Dorset and I have seen one that was found in a wood near Winchester and been shown a photograph of one from a wood in Essex. It is only a matter of time before this animal becomes commonplace in other parts of England, together with its associated problems.

The edible dormouse has spread very little to the west of Tring, apparently because the open farmland of the Vale of Aylesbury is unsuitable for natural dispersal by this tree-dwelling species. Expansion elsewhere has also been slow, probably because woodlands are very fragmented and there are substantial barriers such as urban areas and major roads.

The core of the animal's distribution occupies about 50 square kilometres in the Chiltern hills. Here there are extensive and well-connected areas of high forest (often dominated by beech trees). There are also many smaller areas of plantation forestry, including various conifers, particularly larch and spruce. The plantations and mature woodlands of the Chilterns are just like the favourite habitat of the edible dormouse in its natural haunts in Continental Europe (whereas the hazel dormouse is very much a species of the undergrowth, woodland margins and clearings). Across Europe the edible dormouse is especially associated with beech trees, particularly where they are mixed with spruce. This is an unnatural combination in Britain, where there is only one native conifer, the Scots pine, and this rarely grows in association with beech. However, in the Chilterns, foresters have planted extensive areas of spruce and larch, often mixed with beech. This has not happened on a large scale elsewhere in the country, but in the Chilterns the invader has been provided with an ideal habitat. The edible dormouse would probably not have been nearly so successful if Lord Rothschild had lived somewhere else, for example where the woods are mostly birch or ash.

How many edible dormice are there?

The edible dormouse only comes out at night and it lives high up in the trees. How can we possibly know how many of them there are? 'Too many!' some local residents might say, but this is not really a satisfactory answer. In the absence of detailed studies, it is impossible to do more than guess at the total population size, but fortunately edible dormice are quite noisy animals. They make loud wheezing and churring noises on warm summer nights. This might be some kind of territorial announcement or it could just be a social call, helping dormice to let each other know where they are in the dark. But by walking slowly and listening out for calls it is possible to count how many can be heard in a given distance and also estimate how far away they are. Using a special formula, this information can be turned into an estimate of population density. By this method, one of my field assistants, Andrew Hoodless, managed to show that there was probably an average of about one adult edible dormouse per hectare in suitable woodlands of the Chilterns. This figure is similar to those suggested on the Continent by biologists studying edible dormice occurring in bird nest boxes, and similar to what we saw in special nest boxes at our study site, at least during the early 1990s.

Looking at a map it is possible to measure the total area of suitable woodland habitat that might hold edible dormice and work out how many there might be on the basis of one per hectare. The result of this crude calculation is an estimated total British population of 10,000 adult animals. However, it is likely that edible dormice have already spread to new areas and continue to do so, beyond the 100 or so one-kilometre squares of wooded areas in the Chilterns. Moreover, average population densities in woodlands may be much higher. Over 50 per hectare (2.5 acres) has been claimed in some European countries. Since at least 60 can be trapped in a single house and my own nest boxes (covering an area of only a few hectares) can sometimes have hundreds of animals present, the local population density may be far greater.

So we can be fairly certain that the total British population is at least

10,000 animals and probably quite a lot more. Many residents of the Chilterns would say 'aye' to that, but if the total number really is much larger, then it is difficult to understand how such a large population could have built up in only a hundred years, bearing in mind that these animals have only one litter annually and do not breed every year. On the other hand, it is also hard to believe that the total can be any smaller as it has been possible to kill or capture so many in the past. The numbers at our study site have fluctuated widely but show about a tenfold increase between 2000 and 2008.

Edible dormice feed extensively on berries in the autumn.

Edible dormice and disease

So far, no significant diseases have been associated with the British edible dormouse population. However, its flea can carry typhus and in Slovenia there was a recent fatality from a virus that can be transmitted in the dust of dry dormouse droppings. Since the edible dormouse is fond of depositing large quantities of droppings in certain places (including inside dry houses) this could be a threat to human health. In central Europe, the edible dormouse has been implicated in the spread of Lyme disease, transmitted by ticks. This too is a potentially serious problem, but British dormice rarely seem to carry ticks, so there is little cause for alarm. Nevertheless, it does mean that edible dormice in houses could be not just a nuisance, but also a threat to human health. The hazel dormouse carries no significant diseases, has few parasites and does not live in houses, so it is not a problem at all.

Edible dormice and the law

The legal status of the British edible dormouse is very confused. Under the terms of the Berne Convention, Western European countries agreed to protect all dormice throughout the Continent. This is why Glis glis is a protected species under the Wildlife & Countryside Act of 1981 (Schedule 6), even though it is not a natural British species. As a result, the edible dormouse cannot be trapped without a licence. However, it is also included on Schedule 9 of the Wildlife & Countryside Act, which lists alien species whose release into the wild is forbidden. So, people can get a licence to trap the animals if they are causing problems, but they cannot let them go again! The fate and legal status of any captured animals is left uncertain. It looks as though captives should be killed, a bizarre conflict with the principle that all dormice should be protected throughout Europe!

If the animals are causing a problem then it is possible to get a licence to do something about it. Obtaining a licence costs nothing, but was very exasperating for me because nobody seemed to know who was responsible. If edible dormice are to be trapped out of doors, and killed in defence of crops (including forestry), the relevant licensing authority was apparently the Ministry of Agriculture, but where the animals are a nuisance inside buildings, issuing licences to trap them was the responsibility of the Department of the Environment. English Nature (the Government authority for nature conservation) was also supposed to be consulted. Three arms of Government thus became involved with this one mammal and telephone calls often gave the impression that nobody seemed quite sure what to do. This has now been simplified, but in practice, most people seek help from their local authority environmental health department, but these often do not have pest officers who can deal with dormice. The job gets referred on to private rodent control specialists, who then charge quite high fees for trapping the animals. It is illegal to poison them. Small wonder that householders in the Chilterns view this animal with dismay.

Ecology of the edible dormouse

The edible dormouse is probably one of the least-known British mammals. There are various reasons for this, mostly due to cost. Research is very expensive and dormice are not considered to be of fundamental importance. Nationally, this animal is considered to be of little consequence, no matter what the residents of the Chilterns might say and regardless of its increase in numbers and distribution. Consequently, there is little information available regarding this species apart from what has been done on a shoe-string by myself and my volunteer helpers. Even on the Continent, few investigations have been carried out except in captivity. We do not know whether the animal behaves in Britain as it does on the European mainland, but it is unlikely that the animal's biology will be the same in the cool, wet climate of England as it is for example in the hot, dry areas where it lives in Italy or Croatia.

Fortunately the BBC came to the rescue (see *The Incredible Edible Dormouse*, page 117). They provided the money for me to employ a research assistant for a few months. Andrew Hoodless did a great job scouting out sites for filming, but also carried out some pilot studies on population density and the movements of individual dormice. Population densities were estimated by walking slowly through the woodland, counting animals heard calling. It is curious that edible dormice are so vocal when other species of dormice are silent. They seem to be declaring territory, rather as robins do in the garden, but both sexes make the distinctive calls. Moreover, calling often continues late into the summer, after the mating season has probably ended, and well into the period of autumn food abundance, when territoriality would seem to be superfluous.

Having a research assistant to work full time on this animal was a huge step forward, even if it only lasted one summer. Andrew was able to live in a caravan with the facilities of RAF Halton on hand and a study site full of edible dormice alongside. Actually the RAF were very helpful, despite their obvious security worries about having

Edible dormice are very vocal, often calling at night from vantage points in the trees.

someone skulking about at night in the woods nearby. But this was essential in order to find out where edible dormice go in the course of their normal activities. Andrew caught two adult animals (male and female) in an old stable and fitted each with a small radio transmitter collar. They were then followed for 13 nights. The animals did not stay in the building, although one or both sometimes returned to sleep inside during the day. The male ranged up to 250 metres away, but the female only once went more than 100 metres. This is further than hazel dormice normally travel, but both species seem to move about rather less than other rodents of similar size. The average total distance travelled per night was 523 metres for the male and 111 metres for the female, not very far for a mammal the size of a squirrel. They climbed to heights of eight metres above the ground to feed mainly in beech and yew trees. The male also used low bramble bushes, but the female spent more time in elder shrubs. They were often seen eating the fruits of these trees and occasionally they also took hazel nuts. Both returned to favoured feeding sites for several consecutive nights, then moved to another source of food as the first was used up.

This little study confirmed that the edible dormouse spends most of its activity time, at night, up in the trees. It is particularly well adapted to climbing, having fingers and toes that grip so effectively that they can leap and climb in almost total darkness without falling off the branches. During the day, the animals tended to lie up in nests, built like squirrel dreys or taken over from birds. Edible dormice will also use hollow trees, especially mature beeches which often develop suitable holes naturally.

A few years later, and thanks to the Royal Forestry Society, I was again able to employ an assistant, this time Don MacPherson. He was able to radio track a larger number of animals and confirmed that they spent all their time in the tree tops after dark and seemed not to come to the ground at all. They fed a lot in beech trees, even though they hardly ever used nest boxes on those same trees. He also showed that they did not travel far at night and consistently operated within a home range of about a quarter of a hectare each night. However, two animals did make long excursions into a nearby wood, but then came back again. The animals used many nests, often a different one each day, and sometimes ones that had been occupied by other animals on previous occasions. The main objective of this study was to find out where they hibernated and this is described elsewhere.

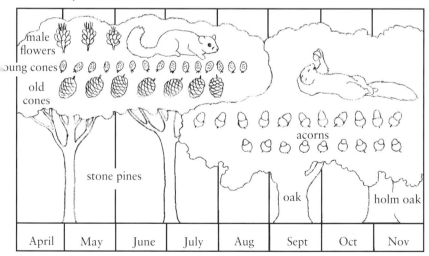

Seasonal change in the diet of edible dormice in southern Europe. A similar pattern is likely in Britain, but using different tree species.

Edible dormice are very agile and make asonishing jumps, even in the dark.

It seems that edible dormice are mainly arboreal feeders, finding their food in the trees rather than on the ground. They probably need a sequence of seasonally available foods produced by trees and shrubs, just like the hazel dormouse. In late spring they probably rely on eating tree flowers, rich in nectar and pollen and their droppings are often bright yellow as a result. Later, when the flowers are over, they may go for insects, particularly caterpillars which are frequently very abundant about July. This is also the peak time for damaging trees by gnawing bark. They eat birds' eggs and nestlings frequently encountered as the dormice explore trees and shrubs looking for food in early summer. In the late summer and into autumn there is plenty to eat in the form of fruits, nuts and berries.

Nest boxes for edible dormice

Since nest boxes for hazel dormice had proven to be so successful, it seemed worth trying them with edible dormice. They needed to be larger of course and it was uncertain what size entrance hole they needed. We used 35 mm, because that was a convenient size to drill, but it was obviously a tight squeeze for the animals and within a few months they had enlarged the holes to 50-55 mm, showing what size they preferred! In the early summer of 1995, we put up 90 nest boxes in a wood near Chesham (Buckinghamshire). They were occupied within weeks, so we put up some more and checked them every month from May until November each year thereafter.

Wooden nest boxes are expensive, especially the big ones needed for edible dormice, so an inexpensive substitute is desirable, especially if foresters are going to use them as a way of catching these animals to remove them from plantations. So we made some 'nest tubes', from modified plastic tree guards, which are both cheap and likely to be available to foresters in large numbers. These nest box substitutes cost less than £3 each, barely a quarter the price of their conventional wooden counterparts. They have a plywood tray slid inside the full length of the tube. Each tray has a vertical block of wood glued and nailed to one end. This forms a plug blocking one end of the tree guard. About 10-15 cm from this end is a block of wood which forms a 'doorstep' partially closing off a nesting chamber between itself and the end block. Each tree guard was shortened by 10 cm to allow the inner plywood tray to project that amount from one end to create a platform, helping the animals to get in and out. Tubes were painted with black roofing paint to darken the interior and prolong the life of the plastic. Nest tubes were hung horizontally by wire loops below a tree branch, with the open end facing away from the tree trunk. The entrance then appeared like a broken-off hollow branch. The tubes looked pretty crude, but the animals seemed not to mind. They were so successful that we later designed a smaller version and used thousands of them in studies of hazel dormice too.

Fifty nest tubes were put up at our study site and the first ones were occupied within three months. Where wooden nest boxes were each

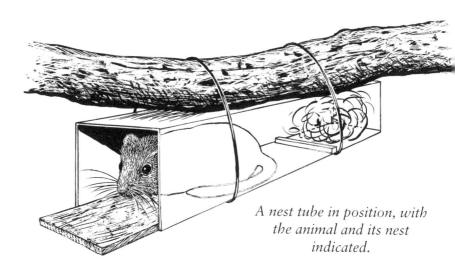

A nest tube in position, with the animal and its nest indicated.

paired with a nest tube, there seemed to be no preference between them. Several animals moved from wooden boxes into the flimsy tubes, despite the availability of sturdy wooden boxes nearby. Among the first animals found was a female that had previously used a proper nest box and therefore must have made a deliberate choice in favour of the plastic tube. The same female was found later with five nestlings and another tube was occupied by a mother and her litter of seven. Both females appear to have given birth in the plastic tubes, judging by the small size of the blind young. A few beech leaves had been installed as nest lining, but both of the nests were very wet after torrential rain.

Nest tubes are clearly acceptable to edible dormice as substitute tree holes in which to live. They are inexpensive and could be installed in young plantations at risk from damage by gnawing dormice. They could be checked frequently during the summer until October (when most edible dormice will have entered hibernation), and any animals present could be removed. If done repeatedly, numbers of edible dormice could probably be minimised and after a few years vulnerable young trees might have grown old enough to reduce their susceptibility to attack, as edible dormice seem to do little damage in mature forests.

Each month a team of volunteers assembles to help inspect the boxes at our study site. Those that are occupied are taken down and emptied into a large plastic bag. This is always a struggle; this is a bit dangerous as edible dormice bite like hell! They are also good at getting out of plastic bags and disappearing up trouser legs and underneath cars. There have been many unseemly scrambles to recapture animals and not a few bloody fingers among those not wearing stout gloves. Nevertheless, in 13 seasons we have handled well over 3,000 animals (excluding hundreds of nestlings), totalling at least 500 individuals. This provides the opportunity to collect information about body size and breeding. We also fit each animal with a special tag that enables it to be recognised when it is caught again. This allows information to be gathered on life spans and to record who lives with who and in which nest boxes.

We can have large numbers in the boxes, over 300 sometimes, but in other years very few. This seems to be linked to the fruiting success of the beech trees. In masting years there are lots of animals, but in the years when beech trees periodically fail to produce nuts only a few edible dormice are present in our nest boxes. We have amassed a huge amount of other new information about these animals, but the study also raises new questions. For example, why do the animals sometimes make big piles of droppings on top of their nest boxes? (Hazel dormice don't.) Why is it that some individuals are recaptured many times for several years (despite the indignities we inflict upon

'It's a conceptual installation on the meaning of life.'

them!) yet most are never seen again. Why do some that disappear like this reappear after an absence of a year or more? Where have they been in the meantime? Edible dormice are supposed not to travel about very much, but it looks as though many of them must do so. Perhaps they go into buildings in years when the woods offer less food? But there are few houses nearby. Besides, how do they know when there is food in the woods outside? If there is enough food in the houses to attract them indoors, why bother to go back to the woods again?

Cohabitation

We often find several animals sharing a nest box. In late summer this usually means a female with her well grown young or a family of juveniles that have not yet split up. This is to be expected, but what is more curious is that groups of animals, sometimes three or more, occur in the early summer before breeding has begun. A study in Italy, using DNA fingerprinting, showed that these groups were usually closely related animals, perhaps family members from last year. It's interesting that they have met up again after the winter, but begs the question of why closely related animals should get together at all, especially at the start of the breeding season, when they should be seeking mates and avoiding inbreeding. Moreover, how did they find each other after the winter? Is this gathering together evidence that they hibernated communally? If so, why did they do that?

Evidence of global warming?

In Germany, edible dormice often turn up as 'guests' in bird boxes. This doesn't cause too much trouble as the dormice usually come out of hibernation and colonise the nest boxes sufficiently late in the spring that the birds have already finished nesting. However, ornithologists studying bird breeding behaviour have noticed that the dormice are waking up earlier each year, taking over the nest boxes at least two weeks earlier than they used to. This means that they compete directly with hole nesting birds and may begin to reduce their numbers by eating eggs and chicks, or by occupying the boxes and depriving birds of safe places in which to live. The same may also be happening in Britain where many of our nest boxes have been occupied by birds (mostly blue and great tits) who then lose their eggs to hungry glis.

116

The Incredible Edible Dormouse

One day a BBC producer rang me up to ask for help in making a special TV programme called The Incredible Edible Dormouse. I tried to explain that hazel dormice were more cute and easier to film and that we did at least know something about them. He was adamant. He liked his programme title so much that nothing else would do! Undeterred by my wailing about absence of information due to lack of research, he offered to provide funds to employ an assistant and to scout for suitable stories and locations for his film. The film begins with a simulated Roman feast, with edible dormice being gluttonously consumed (actually pieces of Kentucky fried chicken). I reflected ruefully that the actors, as members of Equity, were probably paid more for a few minutes of screen time than my assistant received for six months' pioneering research work. The rest of the film explored the anomaly that the edible dormouse is both a pest and a protected species. There were interviews with many people about their personal experiences of the animal and what they thought about it. There was even a memorable butcher who was selling them at £80 per pair for people who wanted something a bit different to eat to impress wives or girlfriends. He claimed that selling dormice was better than battery-bred chickens because they had not been deprived of their sex life before reaching the dining table. This engaging programme was a great success and when it was first broadcast it was seen by over six million people. More have seen it since. One consequence of this is that many people are more familiar with the edible dormouse than our native British hazel dormouse!

Hibernation by edible dormice

Edible dormice are true hibernators. They remain cold and conked out for the whole winter as a way of saving energy. They do this because food in the treetops is not available once the leaves have fallen in the autumn, and they seem not to make much use of foods found at ground level. During hibernation, the body temperature falls to match that of the surroundings. Their breathing and heartbeat slow to less than a tenth of normal rates. The animals become stiff, cold and incapable of normal activity. It takes at least half an hour to re-warm and move about. During hibernation they remain tightly curled up, their tails wrapped over their heads and backs. In order to survive, the animals must lay down significant amounts of stored fat in the autumn. They also need fat to fuel their bouts of re-warming; up to half the animal's weight may be lost as fat reserves are consumed in hibernation.

Little is known about where and when British edible dormice hibernate, but they do not appear to make woven nests like the hazel dormouse. Instead they are found by accident during the winter from time to time, below floorboards, under tree roots and sometimes in outbuildings. Rabbit holes, fox earths and badger setts may also be used. The advantage of hibernating underground is that the temperature remains low and stable; warmth results in fat reserves being used up sooner and fluctuating temperatures arephysiologically stressful to hibernating animals. So it is better to remain cool, but not freezing; only 10 cm down in the soil the temperature remains almost constant no matter what the weather. It is alsohumid, so the animal does not lose too much moisture through evaporation from the lungs. Nevertheless, edible dormice also may hibernate indoors, particularly in house rooves, where many can spend the winter together.

During one small radio-tracking study, my assistant Andrew telephoned to say that the female had 'gone down the drain'. This was no joke, she really had, and did not reappear. Apparently she had already gone into hibernation, even though it was only August 15th. She had entered a broken drain outside the building where she had been originally caught, and her radio signal seemed to come out of several

Edible dormice hibernate underground with no nesting material.

drain holes and also from a spot at the edge of the garden. Sometime between September 30th and October 4th, the radio-tagged male also went underground using the same drain. We then had two sets of radio signals coming from odd places, focussed on part of the lawn. Since radios cost a lot, and anyway I wanted to see what the hibernation nest looked like, I decided we would dig them up. Fortunately, the long-suffering owner of the house was not too defensive of her lawn, although we had no idea how much of it we might finally excavate. In the end we made a hole about two metres in diameter and found both the animals completely cold and inactive, each in a separate earthy chamber off to one side of the drain pipe, about 30 cm underground. The female was in deep torpor, accompanied by a male and another female. Our radio-collared male was also accompanied by some friends, this time a female and another male. Six animals were hibernating within an area the size of a dustbin lid. Both the hibernation chambers were cavities in dry soil with no nesting material and no obvious way in. It appeared that the animals had all followed each other down the drain pipes to get underground. They had dug out through cracked parts of the pipe to create their two nestingchambers and then filled their access tunnels with soil. They were entirely sealed in.

In both cases, all three animals must have entered hibernation together, suggesting some sort of collective 'decision' to do so. Perhaps they were members of the same family, or closely related. Perhaps they just fancied hibernating with friends. It seems unlikely that any of the six dormice could wake up and move about during the winter without disturbing the others. It would also have to dig itself out. More likely edible dormice remain in the same place throughout the winter, unlike hibernating bats and hedgehogs which often wake up and move elsewhere during the winter.

In a later study, my assistant Don McPherson managed to track four animals to their hibernation places deep in the woods. They had all gone underground by crawling along the tunnels created by rotten tree roots leading from decayed stumps of trees that had been felled many years earlier. It's a mystery how they found such places, especially as the animals normally spent all their time high in the trees above, not on the ground. Maybe they follow an adult who knows the way from previous experience?

Anyway, we dug down very carefully to expose the cold creatures and slip a tiny recording device alongside each one. This would store information about temperatures throughout the winter so that we could see whether the animals woke up or not and when they finally left their hibernaculum. Six months later we eagerly dug up the recorders and downloaded the data they had obtained all winter, only to discover that the dormice had left no record of what they had done. They had probably woken up and left almost as soon as we departed. So, the next winter I kept some in a buried cage in my garden. This had got the recorders already installed in a nice hibernation chamber I had constructed. I left the animals undisturbed and they duly went to ground. At the end of winter I went to dig up the recorders and hibernating animals, but found the latter had ignored my carefully constructed nest chamber and buried themselves outside! Again the recorders had recorded nothing.

The third winter I tried again, this time with temperature sensitive radio transmitters. These did work, most of the time. They showed that hibernation was not unbroken, but consisted of bouts of sleep with a cooled body, interspersed with periods of warmth and wakefulness (although they probably did not leave their subterranean nest). At the

'Okay, Madam, so you're lunching at 10.00, choosing a mate at 11.00 and building a nest at 11.02.'

Dormice live busy lives in their short summer season.

beginning of winter the bouts were short and frequent, but as winter advanced the hibernation sessions lengthened to a week or more between arousals. Then with the coming of spring, arousals became more frequent and the bouts of hibernation got shorter as though in anticipation of waking up and becoming fully active again. But they were buried underground, in the dark, where the temperature was almost constant. So how did the animals know that spring was on its way?

Edible dormice are rarely reported active before May, and we have only twice found the odd animal in a nest box in this month. Andrew's animals hibernated in August and we often find numbers dropping off in the nest boxes early in the autumn. In years with good food supplies (especially beech mast) and prolific breeding, a few may be active as late as November (these are juveniles that may not survive, being too small to have accumulated enough fat). But in other years, there is none left in the nest boxes as early as the beginning of October. So it appears that hibernation often extends for at least seven months, October to May. This is reflected in their German name of '*Siebenschlafer*' ('seven-sleeper'). However, hibernating for over half the year leaves little more than 20 weeks during the summer to do everything else. In that time they have to find mates, breed and raise young, who then need to fatten up sufficiently to survive the following winter. It hardly seems possible.

Edible dormouse families

Edible dormice seem happy to use our special nest boxes, and we can then visit them monthly to obtain basic biological information. For example, we find that normal body weights are about 120-150 g, but can exceed 250 g in some of the adults as they fatten up for the winter. We see that some animals have truncated tails, probably the result of accidents or fights. We also see that fleas and parasites are rare, but occasional partially blind animals are encountered. Marking the dormice means that we can recognise individuals when they are found again later. We tried tattooing the ears with a number, but these marks were hard to read and a bit unreliable. So we used injected PIT tags. These are tiny pellets that can be inserted under the skin and read from outside with a special gadget that works like a supermarket bar code reader. It flashes up the animal's number in an instant. We have now had many edible dormice that have survived more than five years and a few that lived at least nine years. This is surprising for a relatively small mammal, but then it does spend over half its life hibernating in a state of suspended animation, so perhaps its body wears out more slowly and lasts longer.

The main reason for checking dormice in nest boxes was to obtain information about their breeding. Babies are not usually found before early August (although Glis living in buildings may breed earlier). Hibernation needs to begin by about October, so edible dormice in Britain have only got time to produce one family per year. Many other rodents, including squirrels, often have two litters per year and frequently more than that. So the babies are quite precious in that they cannot easily be replaced. This is why female edible dormice (and hazel dormice too) seem not to abandon or eat their young if they are disturbed. Mice will often do that because they can go and have another lot quite easily. Instead the dormouse 'pups' will be carried away in their mother's mouth, to be installed in a nest somewhere else. Often the mother will not bother to do this, but instead puts up with our disturbing her again when we visit the following month.

Family sizes range up to 10 or even 11 babies per female, although normally they range between two and eight young. The babies are

*After a few days, new-born 'pups' begin to grow fur;
soon their eyes open too.*

born pink, blind and helpless. They grow fur within two weeks and their eyes open at about three weeks old. The family remains in the mother's nest for about four weeks and probably lives closely with her even after weaning. She feeds them on milk, but she also provides them with a chewed pulp of food from her own mouth. This appears to be an unusual way of nourishing baby mammals, but it may account for the astonishing rate of growth that they manage to achieve, sometimes more than 1.5 g per day. This is essential if the babies, born weighing less than 2 g, are to attain a weight of 110 g or more by about October, probably the minimum necessary to survive hibernation.

Males probably take no part in rearing the young at all. The average family size is about 4.5 babies per litter, but this conceals another interesting fact. As the babies grow bigger in the space of about a month in the nest, their number decreases. This may be because of mortality (falling out of the nest, which is unlikely) or it could be the result of cannibalism. This would accelerate the growth of the survivors. Females are never found with large litters of large well grown babies; many are lost on the way. So, litters of eight or more are only ever small pink and blind. Litters of older babies, with grey fur and eyes open, rarely exceed five in number. So what has happened to the other babies? Is there a bit of cannibalism going on here? Gathering this sort of information is only possible because we can inspect families in the nest boxes; such studies would not be possible otherwise. However, it does mean that as fast as we answer one set of questions, another presents itself. Moreover, we also occasionally find very large families (up to 16 offspring) with a single mother. These appear to be crèches, where two females have aggregated their babies. Why should a female entrust the rearing of her precious young to another animal?

The sexes of dormice are not easy to tell apart, especially when they are not in breeding condition. Fully adult males will have visible testes in an enlarged scrotum, but it's nothing like mice or rats in which mature males look as though they would find it uncomfortable even just walking about. Most adult male dormice, even the large Glis, show barely any enlargement, even in the main breeding season. Young males or non-breeders look very similar to females. In several years, even as late as August, no males were found in breeding condition and there were no young dormice found in our nest boxes at all that summer. This is fascinating because a similar failure to breed had been observed in other parts of Europe, often at the same time as England. For example, in 1996 male edible dormice in Germany had simply failed to come into breeding condition, just like those at our study site. Since then we have also had bumper years, with over 300 babies born in our nest boxes in 2002 for instance. This coincided with a massive beech crop. The following year, there were no beech flowers, few animals in the boxes and few babies born. In fact, breeding failure occurred six times in thirteen years. It became clear after a while that breeding success and failure was directly linked to the beech trees with which edible dormice are strongly associated wherever they occur. It seems that the animals need something in the spring beech trees, probably buds or developing nuts, to stimulate maturation of their reproductive organs. When the beech trees fail to produce such protein-rich food the dormice fail to breed. There would be value in this because few buds means few beech nuts later on. There would be little point in breeding, only to find that the young were unable to fatten up for winter because there was insufficient beech mast in the autumn. In those circumstances it would be advantageous to skip a year's breeding in favour of fattening up the young adults so that they breed more successfully the following year. Nobody is suggesting that the dormice plan it that way, but it is easy to see how a link may have evolved between the animals and a chemical stimulus in their main food plant, making it look like the animals 'know' in advance what the autumn nut crop will be like.

The weights of animals we found in our nest boxes fell into three distinct groups. The big ones (weighing 200 g or more) represented the adult generation. The smallest (less than 50 g) were babies born in the same summer. But many of the animals weighed between 70 and 130 g. This is too big to be born the same year, yet too small to be adults. They are probably 'teenagers', juveniles left over from the previous year. They are non-breeding sub-adults, already a year old. It seems likely that in Britain at least, the edible dormouse may sometimes not breed until it is three years old. This is surprising. Other, similar sized rodents such as rats can breed within weeks of birth and their offspring are themselves breeding within the same year.

Some fat dormice become very fat indeed!

Other aspects of behaviour

Many European studies suggest that edible dormice are quite sociable animals, frequently living in loose groups. Closely related animals may share a nest box and many of the older ones (especially females) come back to use the same nest box (or one nearby) year after year. Edible dormice have well developed scent glands on the feet and around the base of the tail, and are capable of following each other's scent trails even in total darkness. They also have a habit of depositing large quantities of droppings in latrines. Several of our nest boxes soon had large piles of droppings on their lids, and edible dormice living in houses often make a considerable mess with their excrement. Perhaps this is all part of their system of social communication, leaving scent marks about in the form of droppings for other dormice to sniff and interpret, much as dogs use lamp posts. Interesting though this may be, it is no fun when they do it in your house! Hazel dormice (and squirrels) do not make latrines like this, suggesting a difference in behaviour patterns between the species.

In the hazel dormouse, it is common to find animals in early summer in a state of cold torpor. They are stiff, tightly rolled up and appear dead to the world. This seems to be a means of saving energy. Edible dormice may do the same, as we occasionally find small 'teenage' edible dormice (weighing 70-115 g) in a cold and lethargic state. But this doesn't happen very often. Edible dormice probably do not bother to go torpid because it would take longer for their larger bodies to cool down and warm up again, leaving little time for torpor. Their larger body size also loses less heat than in the hazel dormouse, so the energy saving would not be worthwhile.

Predators and survival of edible dormice

Edible dormice have few enemies. Tawny owls catch them occasionally, cats kill a few and some get run over by cars. Otherwise they have little to fear from predators. Foxes or badgers might dig them up from their hibernation dens if they are not too deep underground, but hibernators seem to emit no scent that might give themselves away.

When dormice are seized by the tail, the skin comes off, allowing the animal to escape, but the remaining tail bones dry out and drop off. This seems to happen much more often in edible dormice than with *Muscardinus*. Many edible dormice have a truncated tail, probably as a result of being bitten by their fellow dormice rather than attacked by predators. Some get mutilated while still young, others survive intact for years. This probably reflects social status, underdogs get bullied and bitten by more dominant animals.

We have marked several hundred edible dormice so they can be individually recognised when recaptured. Survival rates are high, with plenty living five years and some more than nine, an extraordinary age for a small rodent, but compensating for not breeding every year.

Some individuals are missing for a whole season, presumed dead, but then they turn up again the following year! In masting years (when beech trees are fruiting well), they are present and correct, but in non-masting/non-breeding years up to 90% of the population disappear. Where do they go? Maybe the absentees invade houses, but then why bother to come back to the forest? Maybe they emigrate, but where to? Slovenian dormouse trappers reckon the animals go back into hibernation, as though they emerge about May, size up the food situation and opt out for a whole summer and the ensuing winter. In effect that means hibernating for 18 months. The very fattest individuals might manage this, but no other animals anywhere in the world hibernate for so long. More likely, in poor food years, they go torpid underground for long periods to await better times, emerging briefly now and again to top up their fat reserves. If they use their underground hibernaculum like this they won't show up in our nest boxes.

Hunting the edible dormouse for food

Despite the name 'edible', few people in Britain have shown much interest in eating these animals. There is not much meat on them, and in any case supplies would always be limited. Moreover, there is a tendency for the British to regard wild animals as something more precious than just 'meat' and there is a widespread reluctance to eat wild mammals at all. However, in many southern European countries, there are fewer inhibitions. In the past, and in some areas even today, the edible dormouse has been an important source of meat for poor families living in rural areas. In Italy, Croatia and Slovenia particularly, the edible dormouse is both common and easily captured. It can be fattened up in captivity using beech nuts or various fruits that humans

A traditional Slovenian dormouse trap hoisted aloft on a stick to attract hungry dormice to the bait inside.

In limestone areas of Europe, edible dormice often hibernate underground in caves, along with bats, where the cool, moist conditions remain stable despite the weather outside.

do not want to eat themselves. In winter it requires no food and can be kept hibernating in a cool place as a readily available source of fresh meat whenever it is wanted. Freshly killed animals are often salted and stored in barrels for later use.

The old Slavonic word for the edible dormouse is 'puh' and it occurs repeatedly in the Southern European literature from the 14th century onwards. This suggests that the animal has been well known and a significant part of local culture for a long time. In some places, apparently, edible dormice were strongly associated with Christian beliefs in resurrection, perhaps because the animals seem to come back from the dead when they emerge from hibernation in the spring.

Traditional dormouse hunting continues even today in Slovenia and Croatia, where more than 25,000 were taken from one forest area alone in 1995. This amounts to an average harvest of three per hectare, but that was a particularly good year for dormice apparently. Each year, in the autumn, the hunters put out special traps on tree branches. There are dozens of different designs and the hunters swear by their favourites, just as fly fishermen have their own trusty lures. The traps are baited with fruit, often soaked in some secret formulation (frequently alcoholic!) and visited up to three times in a night. If fewer than half the traps are successful, the hunter will move them to a better place. Each hunter might catch up to 250 dormice in one night (or so they say), using 100-150 traps. Traditional good trapping places are highly prized and there are complicated rules about who can trap where.

Hunting is only licensed after September 24th. This prevents too many being killed by allowing only a brief 'hunting season' before hibernation begins. Most adults are already hibernating by then, so the cull is mainly of juveniles. In some places the animals hibernate communally in limestone cavities. Sometimes as many as 100 may use the same place and the hunters set their traps outside these underground dens to catch the animals as they enter in the autumn.

Sometimes the skins were used to make traditional furry caps and occasionally skins from adults (which are more lustrous than those of juveniles) would be made into jackets or waistcoats. Like hunters everywhere, the dormouse-hunters enjoy using their skills and sitting around campfires telling hunting tales. It is an important social activity in many rural areas, although town dwellers are increasingly losing interest in these ancient traditions. There is even a special museum of dormouse-hunting in Slovenia. All this may change now that Slovenia has joined the European Union. Part of that process entails adopting European agreements on nature conservation, including granting protection to all dormice and maybe giving up dormouse hunting. Doubtless this will cause grief in some quarters but that is unlikely to get in the way of political change.

The dormouse hunters use the pelts of their victims to make distinctive hats.

Tree damage and edible dormice

The edible dormouse has a nasty habit. It sits on a branch, usually well above the ground and from this vantage point, close to the tree trunk, it gnaws off short strips of bark. It appears that it does this to eat the juicy cambium layer that lies below the dry flaky outer layers of tree bark. Perhaps dormice also consume sap, as various other tree-dwelling mammals do in other parts of the world, such as certain marmosets in South America or possums in Australia. Larch and spruce soon ooze a smelly mess of resin. Perhaps the dormice eat this too, but it is so sticky that you would imagine the animals would not go near it for fear of getting their fine fur gummed up. Perhaps the dormice do not gnaw trees because they actually like them, but because they are forced to do so when more favoured foods are in short supply. Beech flowers for example, are probably a preferred food, but in some years these fail to develop. This is when the dormice might turn their attention to nearby conifers and attack them instead. Anyway, whatever their motives, edible dormice have been a serious nuisance to foresters, causing significant damage to plantation trees.

The principal trees affected are 15-30 year-old Norway spruce and also European larch. Damage mainly seems to occur in June and July. Minor damage is also done to other trees such as Scots pine and birch. Fruit trees (and stored fruit) are attacked too, but nowadays orchards are of declining economic importance in the Chilterns so the depredations of the dormouse in that quarter have become less of a worry, but there could be trouble elsewhere if the animals manage to spread, to Kent for example.

Often the gnawed patch encircles the tree several metres above the ground. This prevents water from reaching the tree crown and ultimately the top of the tree dies. This will often break off in a high wind. Less dramatically, even minor damage to tree bark can result in fungal infections becoming established, again leading to the death of the tree or spoiling its value as timber. This is a particular nuisance in plantations because the trees are all of similar age and quality. If one gets attacked, many others will be equally attractive and suffer the same fate. In just five weeks, four hectares were affected in one plantation and a survey in 1990 of 14,000 Forestry Commission trees in the Chilterns found nearly one in six had been gnawed by edible dormice. This represented a 25% loss in the value of the trees, worth several hundred pounds per hectare. In some places, over two-thirds of the trees had been affected and losses were estimated at £2,000 per hectare.

Similar tree damage can often be caused by squirrels and a common response is to shoot them. However, this is difficult with nocturnal dormice. Squirrels can be poisoned, using Warfarin, which prevents blood from clotting so that the animal dies slowly but painlessly in the space of a few days. However, it is not permitted to use this poison to kill edible dormice, nor any other. Controlling the damage they do, or getting rid of them, is therefore pretty difficult.

Levels of damage vary from year to year and this is sometimes

Edible dormice feed on beech flowers, but may also gnaw bark, especially of conifers and apple trees.

Gnawing tree bark to eat juicy substances underneath.

interpreted as reflecting changing numbers of dormice. However, variations in reported damage might result from more attention being paid to the problem in some years than others. It is also possible that in some years the sap flow is greater, tempting the dormice to attack more trees. Perhaps too the trees are especially vulnerable at a certain stage of their growth especially when the bark is young and thin, and after a while the dormice leave them alone. It is also possible that in some years reduced beech flowering might force the dormice to seek other less desirable foods, and this may be what leads them to attack conifers. This is only speculation as there has been no research aimed at resolving these questions.

Tree damage is reported from Continental countries, but nobody there seems to be quite so bothered, except where edible dormice wreak havoc among crops of Italian almonds. There they put out nest boxes with multiple chambers and go round regularly emptying out the dormice and killing them. Tree damage seems to be a more acute problem in Britain, perhaps because many of the affected forests are plantations where most of the trees are of similar age and type, in contrast to those in natural forests. If one tree is gnawed, many others are likely to get the treatment as well, because all offer similar prospects of food at the same time.

Damage to forestry interests is significant and edible dormice are also a big nuisance in houses, where they make an unacceptable mess and raid kitchen larders. They also make a lot of noise in attics and gnaw woodwork and electrical wires. Perhaps none of this is really serious, but the nuisance caused by edible dormice indoors and outdoors is considerable. To the people affected, this creature is not just a benign and harmless addition to the British fauna. Our questionnaire survey in 1995 sought opinions from people living in the Chilterns and twice as many thought that edible dormice did cause damage than felt that they were harmless. Despite this, opinion was equally divided over whether the animal should be considered a pest or not. This may be partly because half of those responding to the questionnaire had seen the TV programme *The Incredible Edible Dormouse* which portrayed the animal more as a nuisance than a pest and also emphasised other qualities such as interest and scarcity. Perhaps people's attitudes will become less benign as more households are invaded by these animals.

Edible dormice in houses

Reports of edible dormice in people's houses are becoming increasingly common. Three-quarters of reports in our 1995 questionnaires were about edible dormice in houses; only 10% were about observations made in woodlands and 11% from gardens. This suggests that edible dormice in houses have become a bigger problem than in woodlands, where their depredations have attracted more attention in the past.

The trouble with having an edible dormouse about the house is that you don't know what it will gnaw next. Like all rodents, dormice have continually-growing incisor teeth. Unless they gnaw frequently, their teeth keep growing and protrude from the jaw. This prevents proper feeding and may result in death. Gnawing is therefore an essential activity to keep the teeth worn down to normal size. They gnaw wood: rafters are ideal, regardless of structural damage to the roof; painted wood is OK too, but costly to repair. Lead pipes are a good consistency for gnawing, with possible leaks as a result. This sort of damage resulted in a local newspaper headline 'Dormice ate my House!' Even the organ pipes at Aston Clinton Church are said to have been attacked. Gnawing electric wiring is perhaps the most dangerous activity because of the potential for causing fires. Edible dormice were also blamed for gnawing the wires in a Rolls Royce, much to its owner's chagrin.

Edible dormice usually live in the attic, where they eagerly devour stored fruit. They also run about noisily at night, directly above people trying to get a good night's sleep. Their cavortings are said to resemble a football team at play, made worse by the relative quietness of the wee small hours. They wake up dogs, who start barking, and they also set off burglar alarms. One man, who was previously rather fond of his local wildlife, showed me an airing cupboard where edible dormice had nested. Unfortunately they had also used it as a latrine.

Edible dormice seem particularly prone to drowning in lavatory pans and household water cisterns. This results in fur and bones coming out of bathroom taps. People don't like that sort of thing happening in their own homes. One lady living near Tring had 65 edible dormice removed from her house. Several other houses occupied by these animals have had repeated visits from the local pest officers who say they have taken out

Edible dormice are fond of apples, in both orchards and indoor stores.

20-30 from the same house in successive years. Sometimes several hundred are trapped in a single summer within the area for which a local authority is responsible. There appears to be a tendency for edible dormice to congregate in certain buildings. However, it is not clear why the animals enter houses at all. Nor is it obvious why some houses are particularly favoured yet others nearby seem never to attract these unwelcome visitors. A lot more research will be needed before this behaviour can be fully understood and solutions are found to the problems that result. Why they enter buildings is a mystery, so it is difficult to suggest how to stop them. Nobody was willing to pay for the necessary research to confirm my ideas on the subject (that they are sociable creatures who like to cuddle up together, and leave messages suggesting a group sleep in for others to read), so people are left with having to block up holes and ensure that no tree branches touch their house. This is not very satisfactory or effective, as Glis can climb brick walls easily and get in via the roof.

As for why some houses are used year after year, despite repeated trapping efforts to eliminate them, I think there may be a clue in the scent marking behaviour of this species. As described earlier, scent marking appears to play an important role in the social behaviour of this species.

It may be that edible dormice live in social groups and individuals follow scent trails left by others. This is reported by dormouse hunters in Croatia, who say they watch the animals, up to 100 of them, following trails into their favourite hibernation places. They also report evidence that the dormice follow each other underground in the pitch darkness of caves, where they cannot possibly see and must rely on scent or sounds to find their way about. If their multiple occupancy of houses represents an extension of such behaviour, then perhaps once one animal enters a house, others will follow. This might account for the 32 which were removed from a house in 1995, with another 20 being taken out in just six weeks of 1996. Maybe a good house is discovered, like a good hibernation place underground, it becomes part of the social memory of the dormouse population. Disrupting that, to keep the animals away, may be possible if scent trails could be identified and obliterated (or masked by something more smelly). It's worth considering and would be a simple area of research, but nobody seems willing to pay for this to be done. It is not known whether removal by trapping has any lasting effect because there has been no research carried out on that either, principally because of the high cost. In the long term, it will be essential for control measures to be based on sound understanding of dormouse biology, especially social behaviour. Otherwise much time, effort and money will simply be wasted in futile efforts to control this animal. My offer to organise such studies, made to a key local authority, was ignored. I have now retired.

Edible dormice can be captured in cage traps used for squirrels or rats, but they can defend themselves with savage bites, so it is difficult to handle them. Professional help is available through pest control companies, but is expensive. Other practical considerations also limit what householders can do. For example, if edible dormice are captured alive, there is no simple and humane way of killing them that is acceptable to the average person. They could be hit on the head, drowned or gassed by car exhaust fumes, but few people would want to do this, especially to an interesting and not unattractive creature. In days gone by, they could

As dormice are nocturnal, their activities up in the attic coincide with people trying to get to sleep in the rooms below.

be put in the gas oven and killed painlessly because old-style household gas was mainly carbon monoxide, a lethal poison. Nowadays, mains gas is principally methane, which is harmless. Besides, all dormice are protected by law throughout Europe on account of their rarity (including the edible one) so obviously it is illegal to kill them (except in special circumstances where damage to crops or risk to health can be proved) and anyone seeking to trap them is supposed to get a licence first. Having caught them, people are not allowed to release edible dormice into the wild in Britain because they are not native British mammals. The troubled householder is boxed into a bit of a corner.

A tale of two species

The two British dormice, one big and one small, are members of the same zoological family, yet are so very different in almost every other way. Hazel dormice are cute, rarely bite and altogether very attractive creatures. Edible dormice are bad tempered and bite savagely. Our native dormouse lives in beautiful woodlands, alongside a great variety of other wildlife, but never comes into houses uninvited. The edible dormouse also lives in the woods, but these are often degraded conifer plantations. It also comes into houses where it makes itself a considerable nuisance!

Hazel dormice are a fully protected species and it is illegal to catch them, disturb them or otherwise threaten their existence. Even indirect threats, such as those posed by road and development projects in woodland have to take account of any dormice that are, or might be, present and act to safeguard them. Hazel dormice are precious and welcome members of our native fauna. Edible dormice are an alien species and would not be here at all but for human intervention. Although they have not spread far from where they were first released a hundred years ago, they certainly make their presence felt within that area. They have partial legal protection and should not be captured without a licence, because of European protection agreements. But if they are caught in order to remove them from houses, it is illegal to let them go again. They are spreading as a result of illegal translocations and the problems they cause are likely to crop up more widely than in the past.

Both species feed in the tree canopy and among fruiting shrubs. Both eat large numbers of insects as well as pollen, nuts and fruits. Both hibernate for at least half the year, leaving the trees to live on or under the ground. Whereas the hazel dormouse makes a tightly woven nest for the winter and hibernates alone, the edible dormouse makes no nest and often hibernates communally, sharing a cavity in the soil with several others. Both species normally rear only one family in a season, born well into the summer, and both often live in excess of five years. Hazel dormice breed every year, with their success in rearing young varying according to the weather. Edible dormice fail to breed

Members of the same family, but...

in some years, or have huge peaks of breeding in others, cycles that are linked to the food produced by beech trees rather than affected directly by the weather.

While there are many active conservation and research projects focussed on hazel dormice, next to nothing is being done about its equally interesting larger relative, in spite of the damage and distress it causes.

Our work on the small native dormouse has resulted in much public interest and many valuable spinoffs in terms of wildlife conservation. It provides an example for others to follow elsewhere in Europe, where dormice are still poorly known. Conversely, the edible dormouse has been better studied in other countries and we have begun to absorb usefullessons from abroad which may one day help to provide a solution to some of the problems this animal causes in Britain. The exchange of ideas has been helped a lot by a series of international dormouse conferences, bringing together experts in everything from fossil teeth and pest control to DNA fingerprinting and hibernation physiology. On the home front, the hazel dormouse has helped to highlight the need for conservation at the landscape level, not just within small, defined nature reserves. The dibble dormouse is beginning to be recognised as a potentially invasive alien species rather than just a local problem. Both species often turn up in the newspapers and are now widely regarded as core elements of the British fauna. It has also been very gratifying to see the interest that so many people have shown in dormice and their willingness to help study and manage these once-obscure creatures. Thousands have joined in our various research projects. We, the public and the dormice have all come a long way in recent years.

Further reading and sources of information

Dormice are such elusive creatures that until recently few studies had been made of them. The research upon which this book is based was mainly carried out by the author, Paul Bright and others of his team at Royal Holloway (University of London). Consequently there are few other sources of information about British dormice, except those published before 1985, which lack detail and are mostly now difficult to obtain.

Important additional information is available in *The Dormouse Conservation Handbook* (available free by downloading from Natural England's website www.naturalengland.org.uk/). Further information, particularly about legal aspects and forestry can be found on the website of the Forestry Commission www.forestry.gov.uk/. Information regarding dormouse conservation, surveys, the National Dormouse Monitoring Programme and training days for woodland managers is available from the People's Trust for Endangered Species www.ptes. org/. Further information and contacts are available via the dormouse researchers' website *The Dormouse Hollow* (www.glirarium.de/dormouse)

PAPERS

Bright, P.W., & P.A. Morris (1993) 'Foraging behaviour of Dormice Muscardinus avellanarius in two contrasting habitats', *Journal of Zoology, London 230*: 69-85

Bright, P.W., & P.A. Morris (1993) 'Conservation of the dormouse', *British Wildlife 4*: 154-162

Bright, P., P. Morris & T. Mitchell-Jones (1996) *The dormouse conservation handbook* (English Nature, Peterborough) 30pp

Bright, P.W., P.A. Morris, & A. J. Mitchell-Jones (1996) 'A new survey of the dormouse Muscardinus avellanarius in Britain, 1993-4', *Mammal Review 26*: 189-195

Bright, P.W., & P.A. Morris (1996) 'Why are dormice rare? A case study in conservation biology', *Mammal Review 26*: 157-187

Bright, P., & P.A. Morris (2002) 'Putting dormice back on the map', *British Wildlife 14*: 91-100

Hurrell, E. (1980) *The Common Dormouse* (Blandford Press – out of print)

WORKS ON THE EDIBLE DORMOUSE

Morris, P.A. (1997) 'The Edible Dormouse', *Mammals of Britain Series* (Mammal Society, London) 24pp

Temple, R., & P.A. Morris (1997) 'The Edible Dormouse in Britain', *British Wildlife 8*: 349-355

Morris, P. & M. (2010) 'A long-term study of the Edible Dormouse (Glis glis) in Britain', *British Wildlife*

USEFUL ADDRESSES (from whom detailed information about British mammals is available)

The Mammal Society, The Carronades, New Road, Southampton SO14 0AA

Peoples Trust for Endangered Species, 15 Cloisters House, 8 Battersea Park Road, London SW8 4BG.

The Countryside Council for Wales, Plas Penrhôs, Ffordd Penrhôs, Bangor, Gwynedd LL57 2LQ

You must not catch dormice or disturb them in nest boxes without a special licence. Licences cost nothing and are available from Natural England Wildlife Licensing Department, First Floor, Temple Quay House, 2 The Square, Bristol BS1 6EB (0845 601 4523). You will need to provide the names of two people who can vouch for your suitability to disturb and handle dormice. If you already have a bat licence or are experienced in the handling of other small mammals this will help. Otherwise, The Mammal Society can assist by providing suitable training courses.

Index

Page numbers for references to edible dormouse are in **bold type.**